Banjo Paterson's OLD BUSH SONGS

Selected and edited by Graham Seal

ANGUS & ROBERTSON PUBLISHERS

for Kylie

ANGUS & ROBERTSON PUBLISHERS
London . Sydney . Melbourne

First published in Australia by Angus & Robertson Publishers in 1983

Copyright © in the original collections Retusa Pty Limited 1905, 1930
Copyright © in this selection and musical scores Graham Seal, 1983

National Library of Australia
Cataloguing-in-publication data.

Paterson, A.B. (Andrew Barton), 1864–1941.
  Banjo Paterson's old bush songs.

  Bibliography.
  ISBN 0 207 14870 8

  1. Ballads, Australian.
  I. Seal, Graham, 1950-. II. Title.

784.3′ 06

Typeset in 11 pt Bembo by Setrite Typesetters, Hong Kong
Printed in Hong Kong

CONTENTS

CONTENTS

ACKNOWLEDGEMENTS

The estate of A. B. Paterson and Angus & Robertson Publishers for permission to reprint this selection from *Old Bush Songs*; Phyl Lobl for casting a musical eye over the transcriptions; and Maureen Seal for all kinds of help.

Most of the illustrations in this edition were *Bulletin* cartoons which originally appeared in editions between 1897 and 1899.

INTRODUCTION

'The Man from Snowy River', 'Clancy of the Overflow' and the lyrics of 'Waltzing Matilda' are classics of Australian popular poetry. Most Australians can manage a few lines of at least one of those poems. Andrew Barton Paterson (1864–1941), better known as 'Banjo' Paterson, penned 'Clancy', 'The Man' and much of his other work in a style he distilled from his love of our folk ballads, the handmade songs and poems about rural life that just seem to 'turn up' in the mouths of everyday people. From his childhood in the Western District of New South Wales and through the bush ramblings of his youth and manhood, Paterson, at first unconsciously and later with the enthusiasm of the collector, gathered bush ballads. In the mid 1890s he sent letters, advertised and generally enquired after these songs that passed across the country from singer to singer. In 1896 he wrote to a potential helper:

> While living in the bush I used to hear a great lot of bush songs, 'The Wild Colonial Boy', 'Dunn, Gilbert and Ben Hall', 'The Squatter's Man', 'The Old Bark Hut' and so forth — I would like to find out something about these and get the words . . .

Paterson's collection was eventually published in 1905 as *The Old Bush Songs Composed and Sung in the Bushranging, Digging and Overlanding Days*. This was a selection of fifty-six lyrics, ranging from two Aboriginal songs to items like 'A National Song for Australia Felix':

> First isle of the sea — brightest gem of the earth!
> In thee every virtue and joy shall have birth.
> A land of the just, the brave, and the free,
> Australia the happy, thou ever shalt be.

It's hard to imagine those words bawled out in a shearing shed or round the drovers' campfire. But many of the songs in the collection were the real thing, as the original Preface made clear:

> . . . there are many Australians who will be reminded by these songs of the life of the shearing sheds, the roar of the diggings townships, and the campfires of the overlanders. The diggings are all deep sinking now, the shearing is done by contract, and the cattle are sent by rail to market, while newspapers travel all over Australia; so there will be no more bush ballads composed and sung, as these were composed and sung, as records of the early days of the nation. In their very roughness, in their absolute lack of any mention of home ties or of the domestic affections, they proclaim their genuineness.

The songs that make up the present collection have been chosen from the seven editions of *Old*

INTRODUCTION

Bush Songs published between 1905 and 1931. Many of these songs are among the best of our bush ballads and it is long past time they were presented together with their original music. Although Paterson did not print the melodies of the songs he sometimes indicated the tunes to which they were sung. These tunes are given here, together with their appropriate lyrics, some of which have been slightly amended to improve their 'singability'. Where no hint of a suitable tune was given the most common traditional melody has been used. In a few cases I have set the lyrics to traditional airs. All such tamperings are fully confessed in the notes accompanying each ballad.

As far as possible I have let the songs speak for themselves. My notes have been limited to explaining slang, unfamiliar or outmoded terms and to filling in enough of the historical background to bring out a song's full meaning.

Some titles, like 'The Wild Colonial Boy' and 'On the Road to Gundagai', may be familiar. As well as these and other favourites a few lesser known songs from the original collection which seemed worth recycling have also been included. And there are a couple of 'ring-ins', songs Paterson had heard and wanted to include but which he was never able to find. 'Goorianawa' and 'Dunn, Gilbert and Ben Hall' have since been rediscovered and are presented here.

The basis for selection of the pieces in this book was primarily their singability, their quality as songs. Just as important was the extent to which they could be considered 'bush songs'. Paterson had difficulty locating large numbers of ballads and so was forced to include pieces that had little to do with bush life. The already mentioned 'A National Song for Australia Felix' and some similar items have been purged from this selection. Those that are left have mostly passed the two tests of time and singing.

The mixed themes of struggle, hope, disappointment, humour, hard work and a developing understanding, respect and even love for the harsh environment of the bush are entwined through these songs. Paterson believed they reflected the way life really was for the people who pioneered the land, grubbed the gold, overlanded the mobs of cattle, then often 'knocked down their cheques' in sly-grog shanties from Ballarat to Rockhampton. So the songs have been divided here into six sections according to their topics and the times of which they tell. I think this arrangement brings out both the history and the humanity that 'Banjo' Paterson thought so important in these musical stories.

In his original Introduction Paterson described the proper surroundings for the performance and enjoyment of bush ballads:

> ...these bush songs, to be heard at their best, should be heard to an accompaniment of clashing shears when the voice of a shearer rises through the din caused by the rush and bustle of a shearing shed, the scrambling of the sheep in their pens, and the hurry of the pickers-up; or when, on the roads, the cattle are restless on their camp at night and the man on watch, riding round them, strikes up 'Bold Jack Donahoo' to steady their nerves a little.
> ...Heard under such circumstances as these the songs have quite a character of their own.

INTRODUCTION

Few of us will ever hear bush songs in those circumstances. But in singing and listening to them today we experience musical flashbacks to a way of life that now exists only in a few remote areas of the country. The idea of 'the bush' is an important, occasionally dominant, element in the mind of the modern Australian. We are endlessly fascinated by it and drawn towards it, in our daydreams at least. Paterson himself was, despite his bush boyhood and later pastoral interests, essentially a city person, as were most of his contemporaries and as most of us are today. His pioneering concern and affection for what he thought were the musical relics of a bygone age led him to spend a good deal of time and energy on his collection of old bush songs. He was the first serious collector and student of Australian folksong, a still-neglected aspect of our cultural heritage. This collection completes his labours by returning these songs, along with their music, to the singing of the Australian people.

Graham Seal

SINGING THE SONGS

Folk music is basically 'do-it-yourself' music. Just about anything goes, as long as it sounds all right to the performer and to the listener. You may have read, or been told, that folksongs must only be performed with certain instruments or sung in a particular style. That is nonsense. Sing and play these songs the way the people who made them did — any way at all.

You can enjoy the old bush songs with or without the accompaniment of a musical instrument. They all work well with one person singing the verses and everyone else joining in on the chorus. If you want to add instrumental accompaniment, the appropriate chord symbols have been provided over the melody line. So you have all the basics for providing a suitable accompaniment on anything from a piano to an electric guitar, though many people will prefer the more traditional sounds of banjo, fiddle, concertina, acoustic guitar, mandolin and flute, as heard on the record that goes with this songbook.

The tunes of the songs are presented as straightforwardly as possible, so beginners will have no trouble picking them up. More advanced musicians will be able to elaborate on these basics according to their abilities and preferences. Those who only 'play' the stereo can learn some of the songs from the record, released to accompany this book*, in the traditional folk manner — by ear, or hear most of the others on the records listed at the back.

'Banjo' Paterson wrote: 'Ballads do not get justice from cold print.' He was right. But your voices can do the old bush songs justice by releasing them from the prison of these pages.

* Festival L25382

MR. DE VERE'S BACKBLOCK WELCOME.

NEW-CHUM: "Is Mr. Ryan at home?"

LEATHER-NECK RYAN: "That's me, shure."

NEW-CHUM: "I'm going to Myall Downs for colonial experience, and I want you to let me stop here to-night. My name is———"

LEATHER-NECK RYAN: "Never mind your name, it's all the———same. Shure you're as welcome as if it was Ben Hall or Lord Carington."

Banjo Paterson's
OLD BUSH
SONGS

New Chums,
Immigrants
and Diggers

When first I left old England's shore
Such tales as we were told . . .

COLONIAL EXPERIENCE

(by a new-chum)

The events in this song and the feelings it expresses have been experienced by many 'new-chums' since the song was collected by Paterson. Its theme, humour and familiar tune ('So Early in the Morning') make it an appropriate song to begin with.

Although it treats them with laughter, the song's main concerns are disillusion with the promise of Australia, the dangers and strangeness of the bush and the problem of work. These themes are echoed and re-echoed, sometimes faintly, at other times more insistently, through most of the songs in this collection.

When first I came to Sydney Cove
And up and down the streets did rove,
I thought such sights I ne'er did see
Since first I learnt my ABC.

Chorus
Oh! it's broiling in the morning,
It's toiling in the morning,
It's broiling in the morning,
It's toiling all day long.

Into the park I took a stroll—
I felt just like a buttered roll.
A pretty name 'The Sunny South'!
A better one 'The Land of Drouth'!

Next day into the bush I went,
On wild adventure I was bent,
Dame Nature's wonders I'd explore,
All thought of danger would ignore.

The mosquitoes and bulldog ants
Assailed me even through my pants.

It nearly took my breath away
To hear the jackass laugh so gay!

This lovely country, I've been told,
Abounds in silver and in gold.
You may pick it up all day,
Just as leaves in autumn lay!

Marines will chance this yarn believe,
But bluejackets you can't deceive.
Such pretty stories will not fit,
Nor can I their truth admit.

Some say there's lots of work to do.
Well, yes, but then, 'twixt me and you,
A man may toil and broil all day—
The big, fat man gets all the pay.

Mayhap such good things there may be,
But you may have them all, for me,
Instead of roaming foreign parts
I wish I'd studied the Fine Arts!

2

COLONIAL EXPERIENCE

When first I came to Syd - ney Cove And up and down the

streets did rove, I thought such sights I ne'er did see Since

first I learnt my A B C. Oh! it's broil - ing in the

Chorus

morn - ing, It's toil - ing in the morn - ing, It's

broil - ing in the morn - ing, It's toil - ing all day long.

NEW CHUM — a newly arrived immigrant   DROUTH — drought   JACKASS — kookaburra

BILLY BARLOW IN AUSTRALIA

A catalogue of the ills and evils that could (and often did) befall the new settler. Verses 5, 6 and 7 refer to the practice of arresting people with inadequate proof of identity, just in case they were bushrangers. To prove who they were, those detained were taken to the nearest administrative centre where the appropriate records were kept, often all the way to Sydney. This tremendously inconvenient (and expensive) system was deeply resented throughout the colony. Here, though, as with the other dismal events in the song, it is treated with humour.

When I was at home I was down on my luck,
And I earned a poor living by drawing a truck;
But old Aunt died, and left me a thousand—
    'Oh, oh,
I'll start on my travels,' said Billy Barlow.
    Oh dear, lackaday, oh,
    So off to Australia came Billy Barlow.

When to Sydney I got, there a merchant I met,
Who said he would teach me a fortune to get;
He'd cattle and sheep past the colony's bounds,
Which he sold with the station for my
        thousand pounds.
    Oh dear, lackaday, oh,
    He gammon'd the cash out of Billy Barlow.

When the bargain was struck, and the money
        was paid,
He said, 'My dear fellow, your fortune is made;
I can furnish supplies for the station, you know,
And your bill is sufficient, good Mr Barlow.'
    Oh dear, lackaday, oh,
    A gentleman settler was Billy Barlow.

So I got my supplies, and I gave him my bill,
And for New England started, my pockets to
        fill;
But by bushrangers met, with my traps they
        made free,
Took my horse and left Billy bailed to a tree.
    Oh dear, lackaday, oh,
    'I shall die of starvation,' thought Billy
        Barlow.

At last I got loose, and I walked on my way;
A constable came up, and to me did say,
'Are you free?' Says I, 'Yes, to be sure; don't
        you know?'
And I handed my card, 'Mr William Barlow'.
    Oh dear, lackaday, oh,
    He said, 'That's all gammon,' to Billy
        Barlow.

Then he put on the handcuffs, and brought me
        away
Right back down to Maitland, before Mr Day.
When I said I was free, why the JP replied,

BILLY BARLOW IN AUSTRALIA

BILLY BARLOW IN AUSTRALIA

'I must send you down to be i—dentified.'
  Oh dear, lackaday, oh,
  So to Sydney once more went poor Billy
    Barlow.

They at last let me go, and I then did repair
For my station once more, and at length I got
    there;
But a few days before, the blacks, you must
    know,
Had spear'd all the cattle of Billy Barlow.
  Oh dear, lackaday, oh,
  'It's a beautiful country,' said Billy Barlow.

And for nine months before no rain there had
    been,
So the devil a blade of grass could be seen;
And one-third of my wethers the scab they had
    got,
And the other two-thirds had just died of the
    rot.
  Oh dear, lackaday, oh,
  'I shall soon be a settler,' said Billy Barlow.

And the matter to mend, now my bill was near
    due,
So I wrote to my friend, and just asked to
    renew;
He replied he was sorry he couldn't, because
The bill had passed into a usurer's claws.
  Oh dear, lackaday, oh,
  'But perhaps he'll renew it,' said Billy
    Barlow.

I applied; to renew he was quite content,
If secured, and allowed just three hundred per
    cent.;

But as I couldn't do, Barr, Rodgers, and Co.
Soon sent up a summons for Billy Barlow.
  Oh dear, lackaday, oh,
  They soon settled the business of Billy
    Barlow.

For a month or six weeks I stewed over my
    loss,
And a tall man rode up one day on a black
    horse;
He asked, 'Don't you know me?' I answered
    him 'No'.
'Why,' said he, 'my name's Kinsmill; how are
    you, Barlow?'
  Oh dear, lackaday, oh,
  He'd got a *fi. fa.* for poor Billy Barlow.

What I'd left of my sheep and my traps he did
    seize,
And he said, 'They won't pay all the costs and
    my fees';
Then he sold off the lot, and I'm sure 'twas a
    sin,
At sixpence a head, and the station giv'n in.
  Oh dear, lackaday, oh,
  'I'll go back to England,' said Billy Barlow.

My sheep being sold, and my money all gone,
Oh, I wandered about then quite sad and
    forlorn;
How I managed to live it would shock you to
    know,
And as thin as a lath got poor Billy Barlow.
  Oh dear, lackaday, oh,
  Quite down on his luck was poor Billy
    Barlow.

And in a few weeks more, the sheriff, you see,
Sent the tall man on horseback once more unto
    me;
Having got all he could by the writ of *fi. fa.*,
By way of a change he'd brought up a *ca. sa.*
    Oh dear, lackaday, oh,
      He seized on the body of Billy Barlow.

He took me to Sydney, and there they did lock
Poor unfortunate Billy fast 'under the clock';
And to get myself out I was forced, you must
    know

The schedule to file of poor Billy Barlow.
    Oh dear, lackaday, oh,
      In the list of insolvents was Billy Barlow.

Then once more I got free, but in poverty's
    toil;
I've no 'cattle for salting', no 'sheep for to
    boil';
I can't get a job—though to any I'd stoop,
If it was only the making of portable soup.
    Oh dear, lackaday, oh,
      Pray give some employment to Billy Barlow.

GAMMONED — a 'gammon' is a lie. To be 'gammoned' is to be swindled.

FI. FA. — abbreviation of *fieri facias* (that you cause to be done)

CA. SA. — abbreviation of *capius ad satisfaciendum* (a writ of execution). The meaning of these two lines and their use of legal terminology is that Billy Barlow's possessions are being taken from him through the due process of the law.

JIMMY SAGO, JACKEROO

To the ever-popular tune, 'The Wearing of the Green', 'Jimmy Sago, Jackeroo' tells of the contempt in which the 'new-chum', well-bred jackeroo was held by station hands and bush workers. Originally, a jackeroo was a young Englishman, usually well connected, sent out to Australia to learn the business of sheep or cattle farming at first hand. As the song points out, jackeroos were basically being groomed as future station managers. This, together with their usually 'posh' manner and initial ignorance of the bush was a constant cause of resentment — and ribbing — by the 'old hands'.

If you want a situation, I'll just tell you the plan
To get on to a station, I am just your very man.
Pack up the old portmanteau, and label it Paroo,
With a name aristocratic—Jimmy Sago, Jackeroo.

When you get on to the station, of small things you'll make a fuss,
And in speaking of the station, mind, it's we, and ours, and us.
Boast of your grand connections and your rich relations, too,
And your own great expectations, Jimmy Sago, Jackeroo.

They will send you out on horseback, the boundaries to ride,
But run down a marsupial and rob him of his hide,
His scalp will fetch a shilling and his hide another two,

Which will help to fill your pockets, Jimmy Sago, Jackeroo.
Yes, to fill your empty pockets, Jimmy Sago, Jackeroo.

When the boss wants information, on the men you'll do a sneak,
And don a paper collar on your fifteen bob a week.
Then at the lamb-marking a boss they'll make of you.
Now that's the way to get on, Jimmy Sago, Jackeroo.

A squatter in the future I've no doubt you may be,
But if the banks once get you, they'll put you up a tree.
To see you humping bluey, I know, would never do,
'Twould mean goodbye to our new-chum, Jimmy Sago, Jackeroo
Yes, goodbye to our new-chum, Jimmy Sago, Jackeroo.

JIMMY SAGO, JACKEROO

If you want a sit - u - a - tion, I'll just tell you the plan To

get on to a sta - tion, I am just your ve - ry man. Pack

up the old port - man - teau, and la - bel it Pa - roo, With a

name a - ris - to - cra - tic Jim - my Sa - go, Jack - er - oo.

PUT YOU UP A TREE — send you broke   HUMPING BLUEY — carrying a swag

THE BEAUTIFUL
LAND OF AUSTRALIA

Sometimes called 'The Settler's Lament' or 'The Pommy's Lament', this song dates back at least to the 1840s. Paterson did not print the second last verse given here but it has been added from another version to make the story more complete — the disillusioned immigrant goes back home to make a living breaking rocks in preference to the bush of Australia.

All you on emigration bent,
With home and England discontent,
Come listen to my sad lament
About the bush of Australia.

Chorus
Illawarra, Mittagong,
Parramatta, Wollongong,
If you wish to become an orang-outang,
Well, go to the bush of Australia.

Once I possessed a thousand pounds,
Says I to meself how grand it sounds,
For a man to be farming his own grounds
In the promising land of Australia.

When coming out the ship got lost,
In a very sad plight we reached the coast,
And very nearly made a roast
For the savages of Australia.

Escaped from thence I lighted on
A fierce bushranger with his gun,
Who borrowed my garments, every one,
For himself in the bush of Australia.

Sydney town we reached at last,
Says I to meself, all danger's passed,
Now I'll make me fortune fast
In the promising land of Australia.

So off I went with cash in hand,
Upon the map I bought the land,
But found it nought but barren sand
When I got to the bush of Australia.

Of sheep I got a famous lot;
Some died of hunger, some of rot,
But the divil a lot of rain we got
In this promising land of Australia.

My convicts, they were always drunk,
And kept me in a mighty funk,
Says I to meself as to bed I sunk,
I wish I were out of Australia.

Of ills I've had enough, you'll own,
But something else my woes to crown,
One night my bark hut tumbled down,
And settled me in Australia.

THE BEAUTIFUL LAND OF AUSTRALIA

THE BEAUTIFUL LAND OF AUSTRALIA

Of cash and homestead thus bereft,
The ruddy spot I gladly left,
Making it over by deed of gift
To the savages of Australia.

Gladly I worked my passage home,
And back to England now I'm come;

Never more at large to roam,
At least to the bush of Australia.

Now stones upon the road I break,
And earn my seven bob a week,
'Tis better surely than the freak
Of settling down in Australia.

FUNK — fear

A COMMERCIAL TRAVELLER.

SELECTOR (*to "Sundowner" who has applied for the usual night's accommodation*): "Now, will yer jest tell me what yer do for a living, mate?"

SUNDOWNER: "Oh, nothin' much, 'cept travel about."

SELECTOR: "Well, then, mate, jest let's see how yer can travel."

IMMIGRATION

Here's another set of words, on a similar theme to 'The Beautiful Land of Australia' (p.10) to be sung to the tune of 'Four and Twenty Blackbirds' (see music for 'John Gilbert'). Paterson noted: 'Mr Jordan was sent to England by the Queensland Government in 1858, 1859 and 1860 to lecture on the advantages of immigration, and told the most extraordinary tales about the place.'

Now Jordan's land of promise is the burden of
    my song.
Perhaps you've heard him lecture, and blow
    about it strong;
To hear him talk you'd think it was a heaven
    upon earth,
But listen and I'll tell you now the plain
    unvarnished truth.

Here mutton, beef, and damper are all you'll
    get to eat,
From Monday morn till Sunday night, all
    through the blessed week.
And should the flour bag run short, then
    mutton, beef and tea
Will be your lot, and whether or not, 'twill
    have to do, you'll see.

Here snakes and all vile reptiles crawl around
    you as you walk,
But these you never hear about in Mr Jordan's
    talk;

Mosquitoes, too, and sandflies, they will tease
    you all the night,
And until you get quite colonised you'll be a
    pretty sight.

Here are boundless plains where it seldom rains,
    and you'll maybe die of thirst;
But should you so dispose your bones, you'll
    scarcely be the first,
For there's many a strong and stalwart man
    come out to make his pile,
Who never leaves the fatal shore of this thrice
    accursed isle.

To sum it up in a few short words, the place is
    only fit
For those who were sent out here, for from this
    they cannot flit.
But any other men who come a living here
    to try,
Will vegetate a little while and then lie down
    and die.

A SWELLED HORSE.

OLD HAND: "O, I say, it's a bad thing to give your horse so many drinks when working."

NEW-CHUM: "Oh, it's only to cause him to swell, the girth gets so confoundedly loose, don't you know!"

WITH MY SWAG
ALL ON MY SHOULDER

The rush to the gold diggings during the 1850s and '60s attracted large numbers of free settlers to Australia for the first time. But as each new find was mobbed by hordes of hopeful diggers the relatively easily won alluvial gold 'petered out', as the song says. Those without finances to buy the expensive machinery needed to mine and crush the deep gold reefs were often forced onto the 'tucker track', humping their swags from station to station in search of work, food and temporary shelter. The swagman dates from this colourful period of Australia's past.

When first I left Old England's shore,
Such yarns as we were told,
As how folks in Australia,
Could pick up lumps of gold.
So, when we got to Melbourne town,
We were ready soon to slip
And get even with the captain;
All hands scuttled from the ship.

Chorus
With my swag all on my shoulder, black billy
    in my hand,
I travelled the bush of Australia like a true-born
    native man.

We steered our course for Geelong town,
Then north-west to Ballarat,
Where some of us got mighty thin,
And some got sleek and fat.
Some tried their luck at Bendigo,

And some at Fiery Creek;
I made a fortune in a day
And spent it in a week.

For many years I wandered round,
As each new rush broke out,
And always had of gold a pound,
Till alluvial petered out.
'Twas then we took the bush to cruise,
Glad to get a bite to eat;
The squatters treated us so well
We made a regular beat.

So round the 'lighthouse' now I tramp,
Nor leave it out of sight;
I take it on my left shoulder,
And then upon my right,
And then I take it on my back,
And oft upon it lie.
It is the best of tucker tracks,
So I'll stay here till I die.

WITH MY SWAG ALL ON MY SHOULDER

When first I left _ Old _ Eng - land's shore, Such yarns as we _ were _

told, As how folks in Aus - tra - li - a, Could

pick up lumps _ of _ gold! So, when we got to

Mel - bourne town, We were rea - dy soon to slip And get

e - ven with _ the _ cap _____ - tain; All hands scut - tled from the

WITH MY SWAG ALL ON MY SHOULDER

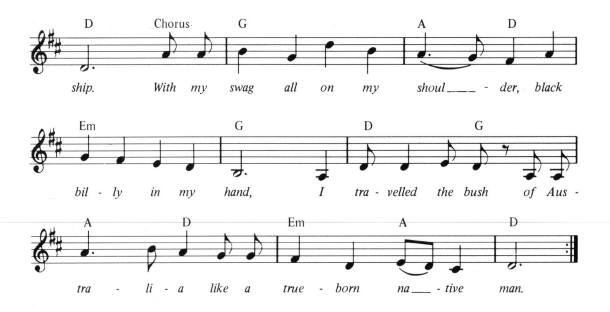

ship. With my swag all on my shoul___ - der, black

bil - ly in my hand, I tra - velled the bush of Aus -

tra - li - a like a true - born na___ - tive man.

LIGHTHOUSE — a particular station that was a prominent landmark in Victoria

TUCKER TRACK — a good area for itinerant workers to obtain work and rations, not necessarily in that order

OUR NEW WINDLASS-HAND.

VOICE FROM BELOW: "Hi, Mike, send down a 'soldier and cap'."

NEW-CHUM: "Gerrout, there's divil a soljer widin fifty moiles of this place. Will M'Ginnis, the polaceman, do?"

HAWKING

The 'hawker' or travelling salesman, was a common sight along the bush tracks and backblocks during the last half of the nineteenth century. On horses, drays, wagons and carts they sold anything and everything to selectors and diggers who lived perhaps hundreds of kilometres from the nearest store. In this song the disappointed miner decides there must be more riches above the ground than under it and resolves to leave the diggings and take up hawking.

Now, shut your mouths, you loafers
    all,
You vex me with your twaddle,
You own a nag or big or small,
A bridle and a saddle;
I you advise at once be wise
And waste no time in talking,
Procure some bags of damaged rags
And make your fortune hawking.

Chorus
(Singing) Hawk, hawk, hawk.
Our bread to win, we'll all begin
To hawk, hawk, hawk.

The stockmen and the bushmen and
The shepherds leave the station,
And the hardy bullock-punchers throw
Aside their occupation;
While some have horses, some have
    drays,
And some on foot are stalking;
We surely must conclude it pays
When all are going hawking.

A life it is so full of bliss
'Twould suit the very niggers,
And lads I know a-hawking go
Who scarce can make the figures;
But penmanship's no requisite,
Keep matters square by chalking
With pencil or with ruddle, that's
Exact enough for hawking.

The hawker's gay for half the day,
While others work he's spelling,
Though he may stay upon the way,
His purse is always swelling;
With work his back is never bent
His hardest toil is talking;
Three hundred is the rate per cent
Of profit when a-hawking.

Since pedlaring yields more delight
Than ever digging gold did,
And since to fortune's envied height
The path I have unfolded,
We'll fling our moleskins to the dogs
And don tweeds without joking,
And, honest men as well as rogues,
We'll scour the country hawking.

HAWKING

RUDDLE (or RADDLE) — red ochre colouring attached to a stick and used for marking sheep

SAM HOLT

Set to the nineteenth century popular tune, 'Ben Bolt', this song gives an unusual angle on the vagaries of bush life. The ne'er-do-well makes his pile and retires in style to live in England, leaving his old mate:

> ...humping his drum on the Hughenden-road
> To the end of the chapter of fate.

'Sam Holt' may have started as a poem by G. Herbert ('Ironbark') Gibson, first published in the *Bulletin* under the title, 'A Ballad of Queensland'. Judging by the many different versions of the song it must have been very popular in the bush, in spite of (or, sadly, because of) its typically nineteenth century presentation of Aborigines.

Oh! don't you remember Black Alice, Sam
  Holt—
  Black Alice, so dusky and dark,
The Warrego gin, with the straw through her
  nose,
  And teeth like a Moreton Bay shark.
The terrible sheepwash tobacco she smoked
  In the gunyah down there by the lake,
And the grubs that she roasted, and the lizards
  she stewed,
  And the damper you taught her to bake.

Oh! don't you remember the moon's silver
  sheen,
  And the Warrego sand-ridges white?
And don't you remember those big bull-dog
  ants
  We caught in our blankets at night?
Oh! don't you remember the creepers, Sam
  Holt,

That scattered their fragrance around?
And don't you remember that broken-down
  colt
  You sold me, and swore he was sound?

And don't you remember that fiver, Sam Holt,
  You borrowed so frank and so free,
When the publican landed your fifty-pound
  cheque
  At Tambo your very last spree?
Luck changes some natures, but yours, Sammy
  Holt,
  Was a grand one as ever I see,
And I fancy I'll whistle a good many tunes
  Ere you think of that fiver or me.

Oh! don't you remember the cattle you duffed,
  And your luck at the Sandy Creek rush,
And the poker you played, and the bluffs that
    you bluffed,

SAM HOLT

Oh! don't you re-mem-ber Black Al-ice, Sam Holt Black Al-ice, so dus-ky and dark, The War-re-go gin, with the straw through her nose, And teeth like a More-ton Bay shark. The ter-ri-ble sheep-wash to-ba-cco she smoked In the gun-yah down there by the lake, And the grubs that she roast-ed and the liz-ards she stewed, And the damp-er you taught her to bake.

SAM HOLT

And your habits of holding a flush?
And don't you remember the pasting you got
  By the boys down in Callaghan's store,
When Tim Hooligan found a fifth ace in his
      hand,
  And you holding his pile upon four?

You were not the cleanest potato, Sam Holt,
  You had not the cleanest of fins.
But you made your pile on the Towers, Sam
  Holt,
  And that covers the most of your sins.
They say you've ten thousand per annum, Sam
  Holt,

In England, a park and a drag;
Perhaps you forget you were six months ago
  In Queensland a-humping your swag.

But who'd think to see you now dining in state
  With a lord and the devil knows who,
You were flashing your dover, six short months
    ago,
  In a lambing camp on the Barcoo.
When's my time coming? Perhaps never, I think,
  And it's likely enough your old mate
Will be humping his drum on the Hughenden-
  road
  To the end of the chapter of fate.

THE TOWERS — Charters Towers   DOVER — a popular brand of knife

BOSS COCKIE: "Give you a job? Why, you're the fellow that set fire to my grass last season."
TRAVELLER: "Yes, but surely you won't let a man's political opinions interfere."

HE MADE 'EM LAY.

OLD UN: "The fowls that come into my place and don't lay, I *make* 'em lay."

FRIEND: "'Ow, Bill?"

OLD UN: "I 'it 'em on the 'ead with a stick."

Squatters, Selectors and Stringybark Cockatoos

The stockyard's broken down and the woolshed's tumbling in;
I've written to the mortgagees in vain . . .

THE FREE SELECTOR

(a song of 1861)

In 1861 the New South Wales Parliament passed an Alienation Act and an Occupation Act, popularly known as the 'Free Selection Acts' or 'John Robertson's Bill' after the wealthy landholder who sponsored the movement to unlock the lands.

When it became obvious to all but the most fevered gold-seekers that there were few fortunes to be made from the diggings by the little man, the New South Wales government was pressured to open up rural land, a good deal of which was held in grant by the established squatter families. For twenty-five per cent deposit, the balance repayable in three years, anyone could buy 40–320 acres (about 16–130 hectares) of rural crown lands at twenty shillings an acre. The established squatters were horrified and resorted to all sorts of questionable methods to preserve their privilege. Likewise, the selectors' methods were not entirely blameless.

The Free Selection Acts (followed by similar legislation in Victoria, Queensland and South Australia) brought the simmering divisions between the old 'squattocracy' and the new selectors to the boil and created the climate of conflict that generated the chronic bushranging of the 1860s in New South Wales and, later, the Kelly outbreak in Victoria. Free selection was also a failure, as songs like 'The Broken-Down Squatter' and 'The Little Freehold on the Plain' poignantly illustrate.

Ye sons of industry, to you I belong,
And to you I would dedicate a verse or a song,
Rejoicing o'er the victory John Robertson has
    won
Now the Land Bill has passed and the good
    time has come.
Now the Land Bill has passed and the good
    time has come.

No more with our swags through the bush
    need we roam
For to ask of another there to give us a home,
Now the land is unfettered and we may reside
In a home of our own by some clear waterside.
In a home of our own by some clear waterside.

THE FREE SELECTOR

Ye   sons   of   in - dus - try,   to   you   I   be - long,   And   to

you   I   would   ded - i - cate   a   verse   or   a   song,   Re -

joic - ing   o'er   the   vic - t'ry   John   Rob - ert - son   has   won   Now   the

Land   Bill   has   passed   and   the   good   time   has   come.   Now   the

Land   Bill   has   passed   and   the   good   time   has   come.

THE FREE SELECTOR

On some fertile spot which we may call our
   own,
Where the rich verdure grows, we will build
   up a home.
There industry will flourish and content we'll
   smile,
While our children rejoicing will share in our
   toil.
While our children rejoicing will share in our
   toil.

We will plant our garden and sow our own
   field,
And eat from the fruits which industry will
   yield,
And be independent, what we long for have
   strived,
Though those that have ruled us the right long
   denied.
Though those that have ruled us the right long
   denied.

PERPLEXING.

THE STRINGYBARK COCKATOO

The hardship of the 'cocky's' life and his reluctance to part with money are constant themes in Australian rural folklore. This song gives us a glimpse of the impoverished reality of the cocky's life through the details of the hut's construction, what was on the menu and the sleeping arrangements. The problems that this sort of living could cause are treated in the last verse.

Some other songs (not collected by Paterson) which deal with similar situations are 'The Cocky of Bungaree' and 'Two Professional Hums'. You will find these in the books and on the records listed at the end of this collection.

I'm a broken-hearted miner, who loves his cup
  to drain,
Which often times has caused me to lie in frost
  and rain.
Roaming about the country, looking for some
  work to do,
I got a job of reaping off a stringybark
  cockatoo.

Chorus
Oh, the stringybark cockatoo,
Oh, the stringybark cockatoo,
I got a job of reaping off a stringybark
  cockatoo.

Ten bob an acre was his price—with promise of
  fairish board.
He said his crops were very light, 'twas all he
  could afford.

He drove me out in a bullock dray, and his
  piggery met my view.
Oh, the pigs and geese were in the wheat of
  the stringybark cockatoo.

The hut was made of the surface mud, the roof
  of a reedy thatch,
The doors and windows open flew without a
  bolt or latch.
The pigs and geese were in the hut, the hen on
  the table flew,
And she laid an egg in the old tin plate for the
  stringybark cockatoo.

For breakfast we had pollard, boys, it tasted
  like cobbler's paste,
To help it down we had to eat brown bread
  with vinegar taste.

32

THE STRINGYBARK COCKATOO

I'm a bro - ken heart - ed mi - ner, who __ loves his cup to

drain, Which __ of - ten times has caused me to

lie in frost and rain. Roam - ing a - bout the

coun - try, look __ - ing for some work to do, I

got a job of reap - ing off a string - y - bark cock - a -

too. Oh, the string - y - bark cock - a - too, Oh, the

THE STRINGYBARK COCKATOO

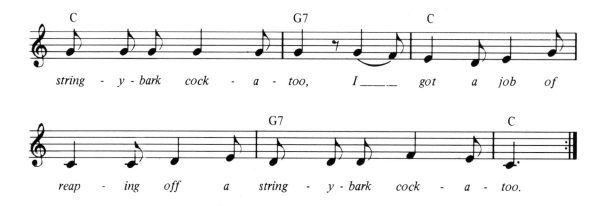

string - y - bark cock - a - too, I___ got a job of reap - ing off a string - y - bark cock - a - too.

The tea was made of the native hops which out
    on the ranges grew;
'Twas sweetened with honey bees and wax for
    the stringybark cockatoo.

For dinner we had goanna hash, we thought it
    mighty hard;
They wouldn't give us butter, so we forced
    down bread and lard.
Quandong duff, paddymelon pie, and wallaby
    Irish stew
We used to eat while reaping for the
    stringybark cockatoo.

When we started to cut, the rust and smut was
    just beginning to shed,

And all we had to sleep on was a dog and a
    sheepskin bed.
The bugs and fleas tormented me, they made
    me scratch and screw;
I lost my rest while reaping for the stringybark
    cockatoo.

At night when work was over I'd nurse the
    youngest child,
And when I'd say a joking word, the mother
    would laugh and smile.
The old cocky, he grew jealous, and he
    thumped me black and blue,
And he drove me off without a rap—the
    stringybark cockatoo.

STRINGYBARK COCKATOO — a farmer, usually a free selector
QUANDONG DUFF — pie or pudding made from the fruit of the quandong tree
WITHOUT A RAP — without pay

HE DREW AN INFERENCE.

SMALL ROUSEABOUT (*who has been employed by Squatter M'Skinney*): "Father, I've cleared out and left old M'Skinney's place."

FATHER: "What for?"

ROUSEABOUT: "Well, one of M'Skinney's cows died of pleuro, and M'Skinney salted her down and me and the other hands had to eat her."

FATHER: "Is *that* all?"

ROUSEABOUT: "No. One of M'Skinney's sows died from sunstroke, and she was salted down and we had to eat her."

FATHER: "Anything else?"

ROUSEABOUT: "Yes; two sheep were found dead in the creek, and M'Skinney made us eat *them*."

FATHER: "They all do that."

ROUSEABOUT: "But as soon as we had finished the sheep, M'Skinney's mother-in-law died, and I was sent to the store for fourteen pound of salt—so I cleared."

THE NEW ENGLAND COCKY

A charming song about the last will and testament of a New England farmer. The 'fortune' he divides among his children is not one of material wealth, but the natural riches of the bush in which he has lived and died. The song is also a tongue-in-cheek comment on the hardship and deprivation that were, typically, the cocky's lot.

'Twas a New England cocky, as of late I've
    been told,
Who died, so 'tis said, on account of the cold.
When dying he called to his children, 'Come
    here!
As I'm dying I want my fortune to share.

'Dear children, you know I've toiled early and
    late,
I've struggled with Nature, and wrestled with
    Fate.
Then all do your best to my fortune repair;
And to my son John I leave a dear native bear.

'To Mary I give my pet kangaroo,
May it prove to turn out a great blessing, too;

To Michael I leave the old cockatoo,
And to Bridget I'll give the piebald emu.

'To the others whatever is left I will leave—
Don't quarrel, or else my poor spirit will
    grieve;
There's fish in the stream, and fowl on the
    lake,
Let each have as much as any may take.

'And now, my dear children, no more can I do,
My fortune I've fairly divided with you.'
And these were the last words his children did
    hear—
'Don't forget that I reared you on pumpkin
    and bear.'

THE NEW ENGLAND COCKY

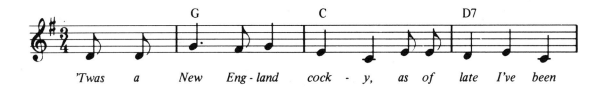

'Twas a New Eng-land cock-y, as of late I've been

told, Who died, so 'tis said, on ac-count of the

cold. When dy-ing he called to his child-ren, 'Come

here! As I'm dy-ing I want__ my for-tune to share.'

THE BROKEN-DOWN SQUATTER

A common story in Australia, past and present. The cocky, selector and even the squatter, caught between financial institutions, drought and an economic recession, had to walk off the land and leave it to the crows and the bank.

Come, Stumpy, old man, we must shift while
    we can;
All your mates in the paddock are dead.
Let us wave our farewells to Glen Eva's sweet
    dells
And the hills where your lordship was bred;
Together to roam from our drought-stricken
    home—
It seems hard that such things have to be,
And it's hard on a 'hoss' when he's nought for
    a boss
But a broken-down squatter like me!

Chorus
For the banks are all broken, they say,
And the merchants are all up a tree.
When the bigwigs are brought to the
    Bankruptcy Court,
What chance for a squatter like me?

No more shall we muster the river for fats,
Or speel on the Fifteen-mile Plain,
Or rip through the scrub by the light of the
    moon,
Or see the old stockyard again.
Leave the slip-panels down, it won't matter
    much now,
There are none but the crows left to see,
Perching gaunt in yon pine, as though longing
    to dine
On a broken-down squatter like me.

When the country was cursed with the drought
    at its worst
And the cattle were dying in scores,
Though down on my luck I kept up my
    pluck,
Thinking justice might temper the laws.
But the farce has been played, and the
    Government aid
Ain't extended to squatters, old son;
When my dollars were spent they doubled the
    rent,
And resumed the best half of the run.

THE BROKEN-DOWN SQUATTER

Come, Stum - py, old man, we must shift while we
To - ge - ther to roam from our drought - stric - ken

can; All your mates in the pad - dock are dead.
home It seems hard that such things have to be,

Let us wave our fare - wells to Glen E - va's sweet
And it's hard on a 'hoss' when he's nought for a

dells And the hills where your lord - ship was bred;
boss But a bro - ken - down squat - ter like me!

Chorus

For the banks are all bro - ken they say,

THE BROKEN-DOWN SQUATTER

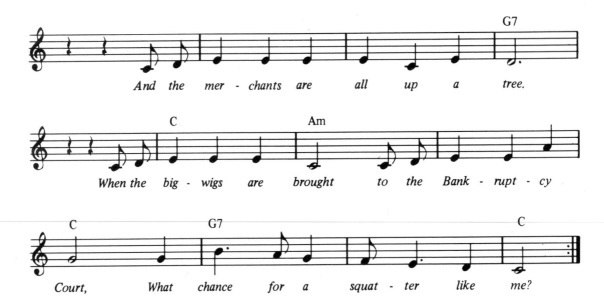

And the mer - chants are all up a tree.

When the big - wigs are brought to the Bank - rupt - cy

Court, What chance for a squat - ter like me?

'Twas done without reason for, leaving the season,
No squatter could stand such a rub;
For it's useless to squat when the rents are so hot
That one can't save the price of one's grub;

And there's not much to choose 'twixt the banks and the Jews
Once a fellow gets put up a tree;
No odds what I feel, there's no court of appeal
For a broken-down squatter like me.

SPEEL — to ride fast

A DAY OF SORROW.

THE LONG MAN (*loq.*): "I say, old fellow, you look a bit down in the mouth."

THE OTHER ONE: "Well, it's about time—when the old woman starts in to cut down your oldest boy's pants for you."

THE FREEHOLD
ON THE PLAIN

Like 'The Broken-down Squatter', 'The Freehold on the Plain' presents a picture of rural decay. The mortgagees, bad seasons and bad luck have forced the squatter off his freehold property and into the paid employment of cattle droving, probably the occupation he had followed to earn the deposit on his 'little freehold on the plain'.

The tune of this song is the same as that used for 'Another Fall of Rain'. But for this song it should be sung a little slower and sadder.

I'm a broken-down old squatter, my cash it is
    all gone,
Of troubles and bad seasons I complain;
My cattle are all mortgaged, of horses I have
    none,
And I've lost that little freehold on the plain.

Chorus
The stockyard's broken down, and the
    woolshed's tumbling in;
I've written to the mortgagees in vain;
My wool it is all damaged and it is not worth a
    pin,
And I've lost that little freehold on the plain.

I commenced life as a squatter some twenty
    years ago,
When fortune followed in my train;

But I speculated heavy and I'd have you all to
    know
That I've lost that little freehold on the plain.

I built myself a mansion, and chose myself a
    wife;
Of her I have no reason to complain;
For I thought I had sufficient to last me all my
    life,
But I've lost that little freehold on the plain.

And now I am compelled to take a drover's
    life,
To drive cattle through the sunshine and the
    rain,
And to leave her behind me, my own dear
    loving wife —
We were happy in that freehold on the plain.

THE FREEHOLD ON THE PLAIN

I'm a bro-ken-down old squat-ter, my cash it is all gone, Of trou-bles and bad seas-ons I com-plain;___ My cat-tle are all mort-gaged, of hors-es I have none, And I've lost that lit-tle free-hold on the plain.___

Chorus

For the stock-yard's bro-ken down,___ and the wool-shed's tum-bling in; I've writ-ten to the mort-ga-gees in vain; ___

THE FREEHOLD ON THE PLAIN

My wool it is all dam - aged and it is not worth a pin, And I've lost that lit - tle free - hold on the plain.

MORE UNION TYRANNY.

MORTGAGED SQUATTER: "We finished lamb-marking at the station last week, and I regret to say the increase is not up to last year's percentage."

HAUGHTY BANKAH (*snappishly*): "How do you account for that? Those dammed unions, I suppose."

THE EUMERELLA SHORE

Another song about free selection. It deals with one of the main causes of conflict between squatters and free selectors — stock.

The selector's attitude was that sheep or cattle should be able to graze more or less wherever they wandered. As the squatters rarely fenced their 'runs', this meant that the selectors' stock eventually trespassed and were promptly impounded, the squatter charging the selector a hefty fee for the release of his animals. In retaliation, the selectors took to appropriating any stray, unbranded stock belonging to the squatters. At least, that's how it usually began. After branding became established, some selectors continued their duffing activities and added brand-changing to their skills.

In the final chorus this rather tongue-in-cheek song rejects free selection farming in favour of the far easier cattle duffing. It's not hard to imagine the squatters getting a good deal of enjoyment singing a song like this.

There's a happy little valley on the Eumerella
    shore,
  Where I've lingered many happy hours away,
On my little free selection I have acres by the
    score,
  Where I unyoke the bullocks from the dray.

Chorus
To my bullocks then I say,
No matter where you stray,
  You will never be impounded any more;
For you're running, running, running on the
    duffer's piece of land,
  Free selected on the Eumerella shore.

When the moon has climbed the mountains and
    the stars are shining bright,
  Then we saddle up our horses and away,
And we yard the squatters' cattle in the
    darkness of the night,
  And we have the calves all branded by the day.

Chorus
Oh, my pretty little calf,
At the squatter you may laugh,
  For he'll never be your owner any more;
For you're running, running, running on the
    duffer's piece of land,
  Free selected on the Eumerella shore.

THE EUMERELLA SHORE

There's a hap-py lit-tle val-ley on the Eu-me-rel-la shore, Where I've lin-gered ma-ny hap-py hours a-way,____ ____ On my lit-tle free se-lec-tion I have ac-res by the score, Where I un-yoke the bul-locks from the dray.____ To my bul-locks then I say, No mat-ter where you stray, You will ne-ver be im-

THE EUMERELLA SHORE

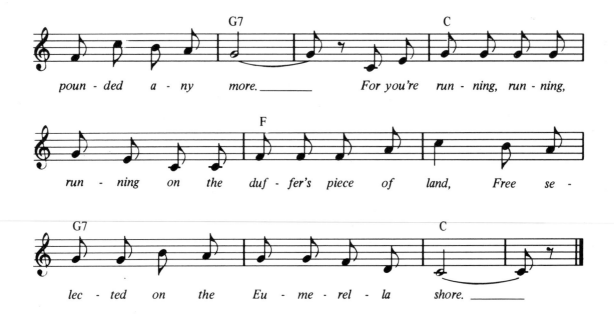

poun - ded   a - ny   more._____   For you're   run - ning,   run - ning,

run - ning   on   the   duf - fer's   piece   of   land,   Free   se -

lec - ted   on   the   Eu - me - rel - la   shore._____

If we find a mob of horses when the paddock
    rails are down,
    Although before they're never known to
      stray,
Oh, quickly will we drive them to some distant
    inland town,
    And sell them into slav'ry far away.

Chorus
To Jack Robertson we'll say
You've been leading us astray,
    And we'll never go a-farming any more;
For it's easier duffing cattle on the little piece
      of land
    Free selected on the Eumerella shore.

DUFFER — stock thief

THE RESIDENTIAL CLAUSE.

(An episode of the recent floods.)

SELECTOR (*the one in the tree*): "I say, look alive, Billy, my son; git over to yer selection quick as ever yer can. Yonder comes the bloomin' inspector in a punt."

THE SHEEPWASHER'S LAMENT

Bush workers of all kinds — timber cutters, shearers, charcoal burners, tank makers and the countless other skilled workers required in a rural economy — were prey to even the slightest economic fluctuations and financial hiccoughs. 'The Sheepwasher's Lament' comprehensively sets out the complaints of one type of bush labourer who suffered a declining living standard during the late 1860s. Like many of the other songs in this collection it brings together the three central concerns of work, disappointed expectations and the conflict between the landed squatters and their workers.

This song seems to work best without accompaniment, or with just a simple melody instrument, such as recorder, harmonica or tin whistle for musical reinforcement.

Come now, ye sighing washers all,
Join in my doleful lay,
Mourn for the times none can recall,
With the hearts to grief a prey.
We'll mourn the washer's sad downfall
In our regretful strain,
Lamenting on the days gone by
Ne'er to return again.

When first I went a-washing sheep
The year was sixty-one,
The master was a worker then,
The servant was a man;
But now the squatters, puffed with pride,
They treat us with disdain;
Lament the days that are gone by
Ne'er to return again.

From sixty-one to sixty-six,
The bushman stout and strong,
Would smoke his pipe and whistle his tune,
And sing his cheerful song,
As wanton as the kangaroo
That bounds across the plain.
Lament the days that are gone by
Ne'er to return again.

Supplies of food unstinted, good,
No squatter did withhold.
With plenty grog to cheer our hearts,
We feared nor heat nor cold,
With six and six per man per day
We sought not to complain.
Lament the days that are gone by
Ne'er to return again.

THE SHEEPWASHER'S LAMENT

Come now, ye sigh - ing wash - ers all, Join in my dole - ful lay, Mourn for the times none can re - call, With the hearts to grief a prey. We'll mourn the wash - er's sad down - fall In our re - gret - ful strain, La - ment - ing on the days gone by Ne'er to re - turn a - gain.

THE SHEEPWASHER'S LAMENT

With perfect health, a mine of wealth,
Our days seemed short and sweet,
On pleasure bent our evenings spent,
Enjoyment was complete.
But now we toil from morn till night,
Though much against the grain,
Lamenting on the days gone by,
Ne'er to return again.

I once could boast two noble steeds,
To bear me on my way,
My good revolver in my belt,
I never knew dismay.
But lonely now I hump my drum
In sunshine and in rain,
Lamenting on the days gone by
Ne'er to return again.

A worthy cheque I always earned,
And spent it like a lord.
My dress a prince's form would grace,
And spells I could afford.
But now in tattered rags arrayed
My limbs they ache with pain,
Lamenting on the days gone by,
Ne'er to return again.

May bushmen all in unity
Combine with heart and hand,
May cursed cringing poverty
Be banished from the land.
In Queensland may prosperity
In regal glory reign,
And washers in the time to come
Their vanished rights regain.

HUMP MY DRUM — carry a swag   SPELLS — holidays, long rests

Wild Colonial Boys

We'll scorn to live in slavery, bound down with iron chains ...

THE WILD COLONIAL BOY

The classic Australian folksong. 'The Wild Colonial Boy' exists in many versions and is widely sung in America, Ireland and the United Kingdom. Here it is set to the tune most commonly sung in Australia.

There never was a Jack Doolan who 'stuck up the Beechworth mail-coach', nor was there a Judge MacEvoy 'who trembled, and gave up his gold to the wild Colonial boy'. It doesn't really matter, it's a great story and the spirit of the song is more important than its historical accuracy.

'Tis of a wild Colonial boy, Jack Doolan was his name,
Of poor but honest parents he was born in Castlemaine.
He was his father's only hope, his mother's only joy,
And dearly did his parents love the wild Colonial boy.

Chorus
Come, all my hearties, we'll roam the mountains high,
Together we will plunder, together we will die.
We'll wander over valleys, and gallop over plains,
And we'll scorn to live in slavery, bound down with iron chains.

He was scarcely sixteen years of age when he left his father's home,
And through Australia's sunny clime a bushranger did roam.

He robbed those wealthy squatters, their stock he did destroy,
And a terror to Australia was the wild Colonial boy.

In sixty-one this daring youth commenced his wild career,
With a heart that knew no danger, no foeman did he fear.
He stuck up the Beechworth mail-coach, and robbed Judge MacEvoy,
Who trembled, and gave up his gold to the wild Colonial boy.

He bade the judge 'Good morning', and told him to beware,
That he'd never rob a hearty chap that acted on the square,
And never to rob a mother of her son and only joy,
Or else you may turn outlaw, like the wild Colonial boy.

THE WILD COLONIAL BOY

'Tis of a wild Co - lo - nial boy, Jack Doo - lan

was his name,_____ Of poor but ho - nest

par - ents he was born in Ca - stle - maine._____

_____ He was his fath - er's on - ly hope, his

moth - er's on - ly joy,_____ And dear - ly

did his par - ents love the wild Co - lo - nial

THE WILD COLONIAL BOY

boy. _____ Come, ___ all my heart _____ -
ies, we'll roam the moun - tains high, _____ To -
ge - ther we will plun _____ - der, to - ge - ther
we will die. _____ We'll wan - der o - ver val _____ -
leys, and gal - lop o - ver plains, _____ And we'll scorn to
live in sla - ve - ry, bound down with ir - on chains.

THE WILD COLONIAL BOY

One day as he was riding the mountain-side
    along,
A-listening to the little birds, their pleasant
    laughing song,
Three mounted troopers rode along—Kelly,
    Davis, and FitzRoy—
They thought that they would capture him, the
    wild Colonial boy.

'Surrender now, Jack Doolan, you see there's
    three to one.
Surrender now, Jack Doolan, you daring
    highwayman.'

He drew a pistol from his belt, and shook the
    little toy.
'I'll fight, but not surrender,' said the wild
    Colonial boy.

He fired at Trooper Kelly and brought him to
    the ground,
And in return from Davis received a mortal
    wound.
All shattered through the jaws he lay still firing
    at FitzRoy,
And that's the way they captured him—the
    wild Colonial boy.

BOLD JACK DONAHOO

Like 'The Wild Colonial Boy', Jack Donahoo stands alone against superior odds and 'dies game'. Paterson noted:

> On the day of the memorable battle Jack Underwood and Macnamara were absent from the party, and Donahoo had with him only Webber and Walmsley. The two latter cleared out when the police appeared on the scene, and left Donahoo to fight alone.

Unlike 'the Wild Colonial Boy', though, Jack Donahoo did exist. Transported from Ireland in 1824-5, Donahoo escaped in 1827 and formed a gang of other escapees. He became quite a local hero until the police finally killed him at Bringelly in 1830. Donahoo and the legendary 'Wild Colonial Boy' are the foundations of the Australian outlaw hero figure who recurs continually through our folk history. 'Dunn, Gilbert and Ben Hall' and 'John Gilbert (Bushranger)' are two other songs from this collection that deal with bushrangers, though there are many more in Australian folk tradition.

In Dublin town I was brought up, that city of
 great fame—
My decent friends and parents, they will tell to
 you the same.
It was for the sake of five hundred pounds I
 was sent across the main,
For seven long years, in New South Wales, to
 wear a convict's chain.

Chorus
Then come along my hearties, we'll roam the
 mountains high!
Together we will plunder, together we will die!
We'll wander over mountains and we'll gallop
 over plains—
For we scorn to live in slavery, bound down in
 iron chains.

I'd scarce been there twelve months or more
 upon the Australian shore,
When I took to the highway, as I'd oft-times
 done before.
There was me and Jacky Underwood, and
 Webber and Webster, too.
These were the true associates of bold Jack
 Donahoo.

Now, Donahoo was taken, all for a notorious
 crime,
And sentenced to be hanged upon the gallows-
 tree so high.
But when they came to Sydney gaol, he left
 them in a stew,
And when they came to call the roll, they
 missed bold Donahoo.

BOLD JACK DONAHOO

In— Dub-lin town I was brought up, that ci-ty of great

fame My de - cent friends and par - ents, they will

tell to you the same. It was for the sake of five

hun - dred pounds I was sent a-cross— the main, For

se - ven long years,— in New South Wales, to wear a con - vict's

BOLD JACK DONAHOO

chain. Then come a - long__ my heart ____ - ies, we'll

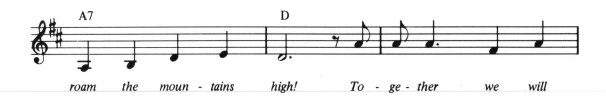

roam the moun - tains high! To - ge - ther we will

plun - der, to - ge - ther we will die! We'll wan - der o - ver

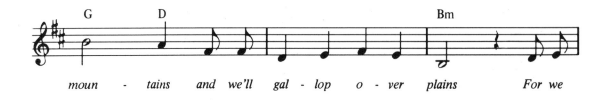

moun - tains and we'll gal - lop o - ver plains For we

scorn to live__ in sla - ve - ry, bound down in ir - on chains.

BOLD JACK DONAHOO

As Donahoo made his escape, to the bush he
    went straight-way.
The people they were all afraid to travel night
    or day—
For every week in the newspapers there was
    published something new
Concerning this dauntless hero, the bold Jack
    Donahoo!

As Donahoo was cruising, one summer's
    afternoon,
Little was his notion his death was near so
    soon,
When a sergeant of the horse police discharged
    his car-a-bine,
And called aloud on Donahoo to fight or to
    resign.

'Resign to you—you cowardly dogs! a thing I
    ne'er will do,
For I'll fight this night with all my might,'
    cried bold Jack Donahoo.
'I'd rather roam these hills and dales, like wolf
    or kangaroo,
Than work one hour for Government!' cried
    bold Jack Donahoo.

He fought six rounds with the horse police
    until the fatal ball,
Which pierced his heart and made him start,
    caused Donahoo to fall.
And as he closed his mournful eyes, he bade
    this world Adieu,
Saying, 'Convicts all, both large and small, say
    prayers for Donahoo!'

JOHN GILBERT (BUSHRANGER)

John Gilbert was the leader of a gang of bushrangers that included Ben Hall, Mick Burke, John Vale and John O'Meally. In the winter of 1863 they entered the town of Canowindra, New South Wales, imprisoned the town's policeman and threw a two day party for the residents. 'All hands were treated to what they could drink; it was then walk up, ladies and gentlemen, singing, dancing, negus (spiced hot wine), punch, instrumental music and all sorts of fun', as one eye-witness described the scene. While these festivities were taking place the unfortunate 'traps' combed the wet, winter bush in search of the partying outlaws.

This rather journalistic song (though not very historically accurate — no one was shot, for instance) nevertheless captures the spirit of the occasion. Paterson was partly raised in the same general area as Gilbert and wrote a fine poem about the bushranger's last battle with the police called 'How Gilbert Died'.

John Gilbert was a bushranger of terrible
    renown,
For sticking lots of people up and shooting
    others down.
John Gilbert said unto his pals, 'Although they
    make a bobbery
About our tricks we've never done a tip-top
    thing in robbery.

'We have all of us a fancy for experiments in
    pillage,
Yet never have we seized a town, or even
    sacked a village.'
John Gilbert said unto his mates—'Though
    partners we have been
In all rascality, yet we no festal day have seen.'

John Gilbert said he thought he saw no obstacle
    to hinder a
Piratical descent upon the town of Canowindra.
So into Canowindra town rode Gilbert and his
    men,
And all the Canowindra folk subsided there
    and then.

The Canowindra populace cried, 'Here's a lot
    of strangers!'
But immediately recovered when they found
    they were bushrangers.
And Johnny Gilbert said to them, 'You need
    not be afraid,
We are only old companions whom bushrangers
    you have made.'

JOHN GILBERT (BUSHRANGER)

John Gil - bert was a bush - ran - ger of ter - ri - ble re -

nown, For stick - ing lots of peo - ple up and shoot - ing oth - ers

down. John Gil - bert said un - to his pals, 'Al -

though they make a bob - be - ry A - bout our tricks we've

ne - ver done a tip - top thing in rob - be - ry.'

JOHN GILBERT (BUSHRANGER)

And Johnny Gilbert said, said he, 'We'll never hurt a hair
Of men who bravely recognise that we are just all there.'
The New South Welshmen said at once, not making any fuss,
That Johnny Gilbert, after all, was 'Just but one of us'.

So Johnny Gilbert took the town (including public houses),
And treated all the 'cockatoos' and shouted for their spouses.
And Miss O'Flanagan performed in manner quite 'gintailly'
Upon the grand pianner for the bushranger O'Meally.

And every stranger passing by they took, and when they got him
They robbed him of his money and occasionally shot him.
And Johnny's enigmatic feat admits of this solution,
That bushranging in New South Wales is a favoured institution.

So Johnny Gilbert ne'er allows an anxious thought to fetch him,
For well he knows the Government don't really want to ketch him.
And if such practices should be to New South Welshmen dear,
With not the least demurring word ought we to interfere.

COCKATOOS — farmers   GINTAILLY — genteelly

64

THE REIGN OF TERROR.
A figure specially dedicated to the admirers of robbery and murder.

DUNN, GILBERT AND
BEN HALL

All the bushrangers mentioned in this song were members of the Gardiner–Gilbert–Hall gang that operated in western New South Wales during the 1860s. The raid on Canowindra is treated more fully in the previous song, 'Johnny Gilbert (Bushranger)', which shares a few lines with 'Dunn, Gilbert and Ben Hall'. After the Canowindra raid the bushrangers attacked Bathurst, the main regional town and there was real fear among the 'respectable classes' that Sydney would be next. It never happened. Hall and Gilbert were shot by police in 1865 and Dunn was caught and executed in 1866.

Come all you wild colonials and listen to my
    tale,
A story of bushrangers' deeds I will to you
    unveil.
'Tis of those gallant heroes, game fighters one
    and all;
And we'll sit and sing 'Long Live the King,
    Dunn, Gilbert and Ben Hall.'

Frank Gardiner was a bushranger of terrible
    renown;
He robbed the Forbes gold escort and eloped
    with Kitty Brown.
But in the end they lagged him, two and thirty
    years in all.
'We must avenge the "Darkie",' says Dunn,
    Gilbert and Ben Hall.

Ben Hall he was a squatter who owned six
    hundred head;
A peaceful man he was until arrested by Sir
    Fred.

His home burned down, his wife cleared out,
    his cattle perished all:
'They'll not take me a second time,' says
    valiant Ben Hall.

John Gilbert was a flash cove, and John
    O'Meally too,
With Ben and Burke and Johnny Vane they all
    were comrades true.
They rode into Canowindra and gave a public
    ball;
'Roll up, roll up, and have a spree,' says
    Gilbert and Ben Hall.

They took possession of the town, including
    public houses,
And treated all the cockatoos and shouted for
    their spouses.
They danced with all the pretty girls and held a
    carnival:
'We don't hurt them who don't hurt us,' says
    Gilbert and Ben Hall.

DUNN, GILBERT AND BEN HALL

Come all you wild co - lo - ni - als and list - en to my

tale, A sto - ry of bush - rang - ers' deeds I

will to you un - veil. 'Tis of those gall - ant

her - oes, game fight - ers one and all; And we'll

sit and sing 'Long live the King, Dunn, Gil - bert and Ben Hall.'

DUNN, GILBERT AND BEN HALL

Then Miss O'Flanagan performed in a manner quite genteelly,
Upon the grand 'pianner' for the bushranger O'Meally.
'Roll up, roll up, it's just a lark for women, kids and all;
We'll rob the rich and help the poor,' says Gilbert and Ben Hall.

They made a raid on Bathurst, the pace was getting hot;
But Johnny Vane surrendered after Mickey Burke was shot.
O'Meally at Goimbla did like a hero fall;
'The game is getting lively,' says Gilbert and Ben Hall.

Then Gilbert took a holiday, Ben Hall got new recruits;
The 'Old Man' and Dunleavy shared in the plunder's fruits.
Then Dunleavy he surrendered and they jugged the 'Old Man' tall,
So Johnny Gilbert came again to help his mate, Ben Hall.

John Dunn he was a jockey, a-riding all the winners,
Until he joined Hall's gang to rob the publicans and sinners.
And many a time the Royal Mail bailed up at John Dunn's call;
A thousand pounds is on their heads, Dunn, Gilbert and Ben Hall.

'Hand over all your watches and the banknotes in your purses,
All travellers must pay toll to us, we don't care for your curses.
We are the rulers of the roads, we've seen the troopers fall,
And we want your gold and money,' says Dunn, Gilbert and Ben Hall.

'Next week we'll visit Goulburn and clean the banks out there,
So if you see the peelers just tell them to beware.
And then to Sydney city we mean to pay a call,
And we'll take the whole damn' country,' says Dunn, Gilbert and Ben Hall.

FRANK GARDINER — The most notorious bushranger of the period. He masterminded the Eugowra Rocks robbery of the Forbes gold escort in 1862, the nineteenth century Australian equivalent of the Great Train Robbery.

KITTY BROWN — Gardiner's mistress. She inadvertently betrayed Gardiner and testified against him at his trial.

SIR FRED — Sir Frederick Pottinger, Bt., Inspector of Police in the Western District of New South Wales from 1862 until 1865. His continued failure to capture Gardiner and the other local bushrangers had made him a laughing stock. He was on his way to Sydney to defend himself against dismissal from the police force when he accidentally shot himself, dying from the wound a few days later.

BUSHRANGING VAGARIES IN N.S.W.

Shanties, Sprees and Swaggies

I'm crook in the head, for I haven't been to bed ...

THE JOLLY, JOLLY GROG
AND TOBACCO

Usually known as 'Across the Western Plains', this song is descended from an earlier sea-song called 'Across the Western Oceans'. The subject of both is the hangover of all time. After receiving his lump sum payment for a season's work the sufferer in this song gets waylaid at a 'shanty', an illegal drinking house, and proceeds to 'knock down his cheque'. The results are graphically presented in the song—alcoholic remorse, groggy repentance then back to the inevitable cycle of tramping the track, erratic seasonal work, another spree, and so on . . .

I'm stiff and stony broke, and I've parted with
    my moke,
And the sky is looking black as thunder,
And the boss of the shanty too, for I haven't
    a sou—
That's the way you're treated when you're
    down and under.

Chorus
It's ah! for my grog, my jolly, jolly grog,
It's ah! for my beer and tobacco,
I spent all my tin in the shanty drinking gin,
Now across the western plains I must wander.

I'm crook in the head, for I haven't been to
    bed,
Since first I touched this shanty with my
    plunder,
I see centipedes and snakes, and I'm full of
    aches and shakes,
So I'd better make a push out over yonder.

I take the Old Man Plain, criss-cross it all
    again,
Until my eyes the track no longer see,
My beer and brandy brain seeks balmy sleep in
    vain,
I feel as if I had the Darling Pea.

Repentance brings reproof, so I sadly 'pad the
    hoof',
All day I see the mirage of the trees,
But it all will have an end when I reach the
    river bend,
And listen to the sighing of the breeze.

Then hang the jolly prog, the hocussed shanty
    grog,
The beer that's loaded with tobacco,
Grafting humour I am in, and I'll stick the peg
    right in
And settle once more down to Yakka.

THE JOLLY, JOLLY GROG AND TOBACCO

I'm stiff and sto - ny broke, and I've part - ed with my

moke, _____ And the sky is look - ing black as thun - der, _____

_____ And the boss of the shan - ty too, for I have - n't a

sou _____ That's the way you're treat - ed when you're down and un -

der. It's _____ ah! for my grog, my jol - ly, jol - ly,

grog, It's ah! for my beer and to - bac - co, _____ I

THE JOLLY, JOLLY GROG AND TOBACCO

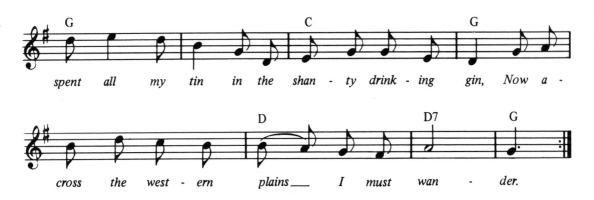

spent all my tin in the shan - ty drink - ing gin, Now a -
cross the west - ern plains ___ I must wan - der.

MOKE — horse

HAD THE DARLING PEA — in a bad mood. Derived from a poisonous plant of the Darling River region
which causes animals that eat it to stagger and, finally, die.

PROG — usually 'food', but here equivalent to 'grog'

HOCUSSED — drugged

YAKKA — work

AN INVERTED VIEW.

SHE: "If I were you I would go without drinking."

OLD TOPER: "Hic! if you were me, Miss, you would drink without going. Mine's beer."

ON THE ROAD TO GUNDAGAI

Yet another saga of the ever-popular spree. This one took place at Lazy Harry's shanty near Gundagai, New South Wales, after the shearing was over. The spree lasted a week and then the shearers tramped back to work, broke and bleary.

The mention of 'beer to knock you sideways' probably refers to the common shanty practice of drugging or 'hocussing' the liquor in order to knock the drinkers out so that they could be robbed by 'the girls to make you sigh'. The same practice is mentioned in 'The Jolly, Jolly Grog and Tobacco' where the grog is laced with tobacco.

Oh, we started down from Roto when the
    sheds had all cut out.
We'd whips and whips of rhino as we meant to
    push about,
So we humped our blues serenely and made for
    Sydney town,
With a three-spot cheque between us, as
    wanted knocking down.

Chorus
But we camped at Lazy Harry's, on the road to
    Gundagai,
The road to Gundagai, not five miles from
    Gundagai.
Yes, we camped at Lazy Harry's, on the road
    to Gundagai.

Well, we struck the Murrumbidgee near the
    Yanco in a week,
And passed through old Narrandera and crossed
    the Burnett Creek.

And we never stopped at Wagga, for we'd
    Sydney in our eye.
But we camped at Lazy Harry's, on the road to
    Gundagai.

Oh, I've seen a lot of girls, my boys, and
    drunk a lot of beer,
And I've met with some of both, chaps, as has
    left me mighty queer;
But for beer to knock you sideways, and for
    girls to make you sigh,
You must camp at Lazy Harry's, on the road
    to Gundagai.

Well, we chucked our blooming swags off, and
    we walked into the bar,
And we called for rum-an'-raspb'ry and a
    shilling each cigar.
But the girl that served the pizen, she winked
    at Bill and I—
And we camped at Lazy Harry's, not five miles
    from Gundagai.

ON THE ROAD TO GUNDAGAI

Oh, we start - ed down from Ro - to when the sheds had all cut out. We'd __ whips and whips of rhi - no as we meant to push a - bout, So we humped our blues se - rene - ly and made for Syd - ney town, With a three - spot cheque be - tween us, as want - ed knock - ing down. But we camped at La - zy Har - ry's, on the

ON THE ROAD TO GUNDAGAI

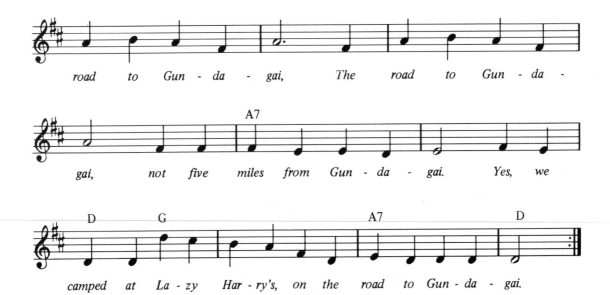

road to Gun - da - gai, The road to Gun - da - gai, not five miles from Gun - da - gai. Yes, we camped at La - zy Har - ry's, on the road to Gun - da - gai.

In a week the spree was over and the cheque
    was all knocked down,
So we shouldered our Matildas, and we turned
    our back on town,
And the girls they stood a nobbler as we sadly
    said good-bye,

And we tramped from Lazy Harry's, not five
    miles from Gundagai;

Last chorus
And we tramped from Lazy Harry's, not five
    miles from Gundagai.

RHINO — money
PIZEN — usually poison but here meaning alcohol
MATILDA — a swag
NOBBLER — a measure of spirits

"ONE TOUCH OF NATURE" ETC.

TRAVELLER: "I say, boss, is there any empty hut a cove could camp in to-night? It looks like rain."

SQUATTER: "Well, yes. There's the Chinamen's hut down there; you can doss with them if they'll let you—*I* don't object."

THE WALLABY BRIGADE

The 'Wallaby Brigade' and the 'Tag-rag Band' are terms for the army of itinerant workers who tramped the bush of Australia between the golden fifties and the First World War. This song gives some glimpses into the seamier side of being 'on the wallaby'. Stations which refused the wandering swaggie his rations ran the risk of having their fences fired or of losing a whole sheep when the hungry wanderer, a kilometre or two along the track, would 'knock a monkey over' for his supper.

You often have been told of regiments brave
    and bold,
But we are the bravest in the land;
We're called the Tag-rag Band, and we rally in
    Queensland,
We are members of the Wallaby Brigade.

Chorus
Tramp, tramp, tramp across the borders,
The swagmen are rolling up, I see.
When the shearing's at an end we'll go fishing
    in a bend.
Then hurrah! for the Wallaby Brigade.

When you are leaving camp, you must ask
    some brother tramp
If there are any jobs to be had,
Or what sort of a shop that station is to stop
For a member of the Wallaby Brigade.

You ask if they want men, you ask for rations
    then—
If they don't stump up a warning should be made;
To teach them better sense—why, 'Set fire to
    their fence'
Is the war cry of the Wallaby Brigade.

The squatters thought us done when they
    fenced in all their run,
But a prettier mistake they never made;
You've only to sport your dover and knock a
    monkey over—
There's cheap mutton for the Wallaby Brigade.

Now when the shearing's in our harvest will
    begin,
Our swags for a spell down will be laid;
But when our cheques are drank we will join
    the Tag-rag rank,
Limeburners in the Wallaby Brigade.

DOVER — brand name of a popular knife

MONKEY — sheep

THE WALLABY BRIGADE

You of-ten have been told of re-gi-ments brave and

bold, But we are the bra-vest in the land;___

___ We're called the Tag-rag Band, and we ral-ly in Queens-

land, We are mem-bers of the Wal-la-by Bri-gade.___

Chorus

___ Tramp, tramp, tramp a-cross the bord-ers, The

swag-men are roll-ing up, I see.___ When the

THE WALLABY BRIGADE

shear - ing's   at   an   end   we'll   go   fish - ing   in   a

bend.   Then   hur - rah!   for   the   Wal - la - by   Bri - gade._____

HE LIKED IT HOT.

JACK: "That's good grog, Bill; always good when yer see that kind'r oily stuff in it."

BILL: "I wouldn't give a darn for it. I like it when what drops off yer beard makes brown holes in the front of yer shirt."

THE OLD BARK HUT

The story of Bob the Swagman and the delights of living in an old bark hut. This colourful song begins to develop into a yarn, a tall tale, towards the end when we learn about Bob's flea problems. It probably wouldn't be going too far to assume that Bob had been drinking, a subject discreetly avoided in the song.

'Ten pounds of flour, ten pounds of beef, some sugar and some tea' refers to the standard ration a station allowed swagmen for the week. There is a 'swagman's toast' that refers to these rations in terms similar to those used in the song:

> A little bit of sugar and a little bit of tea
> A little bit of flour you can hardly see
> And a little bit of meat for you and me —
> It's a bugger of a life, by Jesus!

Oh, my name is Bob the Swagman, before
    you all I stand,
And I've had many ups and downs while
    travelling through the land.
I once was well-to-do, my boys, but now I am
    stumped up,
And I'm forced to go on rations in an old bark
    hut.

Chorus
In an old bark hut, in an old bark hut.
I'm forced to go on rations in an old bark hut.

Ten pounds of flour, ten pounds of beef,
    some sugar and some tea,
That's all they give to a hungry man, until the
    Seventh Day.

If you don't be mighty sparing, you'll go with
    a hungry gut—
For that's one of the great misfortunes in an
    old bark hut.

Chorus
In an old bark hut, in an old bark hut.
For that's one of the great misfortunes in an
    old bark hut.

The bucket you boil your beef in has to carry
    water, too,
And they'll say you're getting mighty flash if
    you should ask for two.
I've a billy, and a pint-pot, and a broken-
    handled cup,
And they all adorn the table in the old bark
    hut.

THE OLD BARK HUT

Oh, my name is Bob the Swag - man, be - fore you all I

stand, And I've had ma - ny ups and downs while trav' - ling through the

land. I once was well - to - do, my boys, but now I am stumped

up, And I'm forced to go on ra - tions in an old bark hut.

Chorus

In an old bark hut, in an old bark hut. I'm

forced to go on ra - tions in an old bark hut.

THE OLD BARK HUT

Chorus
In an old bark hut, in an old bark hut.
And they all adorn the table in the old bark
hut.

Faith, the table is not made of wood, as many
you have seen—
For if I had one half so good, I'd think myself
serene—
'Tis only an old sheet of bark—God knows
when it was cut—
It was blown from off the rafters of the old
bark hut.

Chorus
In an old bark hut, in an old bark hut.
It was blown from off the rafters of the old
bark hut.

And of furniture, there's no such thing, 'twas
never in the place,
Except the stool I sit upon—and that's an old
gin-case.
It does us for a safe as well, but you must keep
it shut,
Or the flies would make it canter round the old
bark hut.

Chorus
In an old bark hut, in an old bark hut.
Or the flies would make it canter round the
old bark hut.

If you should leave it open, and the flies should
find your meat,
They'll scarcely leave a single piece that's fit for
man to eat.

But you mustn't curse, nor grumble—what
won't fatten will fill up—
For what's out of sight is out of mind in an
old bark hut.

Chorus
In an old bark hut, in an old bark hut.
For what's out of sight is out of mind in an
old bark hut.

In the summertime when the weather's warm
this hut is nice and cool,
And you'll find the gentle breezes blowing in
through every hole.
You can leave the old door open, or you can
leave it shut,
There's no fear of suffocation in the old bark
hut.

Chorus
In an old bark hut, in an old bark hut.
There's no fear of suffocation in the old bark
hut.

In the winter-time—preserve us all!—to live in
there's a treat,
Especially when it's raining hard, and blowing
wind and sleet.
The rain comes down the chimney, and your
meat is black with soot—
That's a substitute for pepper in an old bark
hut.

Chorus
In an old bark hut, in an old bark hut.
That's a substitute for pepper in an old bark
hut.

THE OLD BARK HUT

I've seen the rain come in this hut just like a
    perfect flood,
Especially through that great big hole where
    once the table stood.
There's not a blessed spot, me boys, where you
    could lay your nut,
But the rain is sure to find you in the old bark
    hut.

Chorus
In an old bark hut, in an old bark hut.
But the rain is sure to find you in the old bark
    hut.

So beside the fire I make me bed, and there I
    lay me down,
And think myself as happy as the king that
    wears a crown.
But as you'd be dozing off to sleep a flea will
    wake you up,
Which makes you curse the vermin in the old
    bark hut.

Chorus
In an old bark hut, in an old bark hut.
Which makes you curse the vermin in the old
    bark hut.

Faith, such flocks of fleas you never saw, they
    are so plump and fat,
And if you make a grab at one, he'll spit just
    like a cat.
Last night they got my pack of cards, and were
    fighting for the cut—
I thought the Devil had me in the old bark
    hut.

Chorus
In an old bark hut, in an old bark hut.
I thought the Devil had me in the old bark
    hut.

So now, my friends, I've sung my song, and
    that as well as I could,
And I hope the ladies present won't think my
    language rude,
And all ye younger people, in the days when
    you grow up,
Remember Bob the Swagman, and the old bark
    hut.

Chorus
In an old bark hut, in an old bark hut.
Remember Bob the Swagman, and the old bark
    hut.

SAFE — meat safe, the nineteenth century version of the refrigerator

THE RAMBLE-EER

The 'rambling rake' figure is a common one in British and American balladry — have a look at 'Rover No More', for example. Like the 'Murrumbidgee Shearer' the rake has followed a variety of trades and occupations, some of which he would rather not recall. But in spite of that, he claims never to have stooped to 'lambing-down', the not-so-gentle art of parting the bush worker from his hard-earned cheque.

The earth rolls on through empty space, its
    journey's never done,
It's entered for a starry race throughout the
    Kingdom Come.
And, as I am a bit of earth, I follow it
    because—
And I prove I am a rolling stone and never
    gather moss.

Chorus
For I am a ramble-eer, a rollicking ramble-eer,
I'm a roving rake of poverty and son of a gun
    for beer.

I've done a bit of fossicking for tucker and for
    gold;
I've been a menial rouseabout and a rollicking
    shearer bold,
I've 'shanked' across the Old Man Plain, after
    busting up a cheque,

And 'whipped the cat' once more again,
    though I haven't met it yet.

I've done a bit of droving of cattle and of
    sheep,
And I've done a bit of moving with Matilda for
    a mate;
Of fencing I have done my share, wool-
    scouring on the green;
Axeman, navvy—Old Nick can bear out what I
    haven't been.

I've worked the treadmill thresher, the scythe
    and reaping-hook,
Been wood-and-water fetcher for Mary Jane
    the cook;
I've done a few 'cronk' things too, when I
    have struck a town,
There's few things I wouldn't do—but I never
    did lambing-down.

THE RAMBLE-EER

The earth rolls on through emp - ty space, its jour - ney's ne - ver

done, It's en - tered for a star - ry race through -

out the King - dom Come. And, as I am a

bit of earth, I fol - low it be - cause And I

prove I am a roll - ing stone and ne - ver ga - ther

THE RAMBLE-EER

moss.   For I am a ram - ble - eer, a rol - lick - ing ram - ble - eer, I'm a rov - ing rake of po - ver - ty and a son of a gun for beer.

FOSSICKING — usually prospecting for gold, but here also means scratching around for food

SHANKED — walked, as in the expression 'Shanks' pony'

BUSTING UP A CHEQUE — spending all his money on a 'spree'

WHIPPED THE CAT — complained or 'whinged'. The meaning of this line seems to be that the Ramble-eer has often complained about many things but without much reason.

MATILDA — swag

CRONK — worthless, shady; similar to 'crook'

LAMBING-DOWN — see p. 88

NOT CURRENCY.

HE: "I'm goin' to shout for the boy—I s'pose my name's good?"
MR. BUNG: "Well, you see, it ain't cash."

FOUR LITTLE JOHNNY CAKES

A 'johnny cake' is a small damper or scone cooked on, rather than in, the ashes of a campfire. Here's a recipe for johnny cakes:

Mix 250 g of plain flour with 1 tablespoon (20 ml) of baking powder and 1 teaspoon (5 ml) of salt. Slowly add water to this mixture until it goes stiff and doughy. Make this dough into cakes about 12 cm by 2.5 cm and fry in pan about 10 minutes each side, or place on ashes of fire. Eat them cold with jam, honey or 'cockies' joy' — golden syrup.

The song is an idealised account of the bushworker's easy life between bouts of work. In this case the lucky man is a shearer.

Hurrah for the Lachlan, boys, and join me in
    a cheer;
That's the place to go to make an easy cheque
    ev'ry year;
With a toad-skin in me pocket I borrowed
    from a friend,
Oh, isn't it nice and cosy to be campin' in the
    bend?

Chorus
With me little round flour bag sittin' on a
    stump,
Me little tea and sugar bag a-looking nice and
    plump;
With a little fat codfish just off the hook,
And four little johnny cakes, a credit to the
    cook.

I've a loaf or two of bread, and some
    'murphies' that I shook,

Perhaps a loaf of brownie that I snavelled from
    the cook,
A nice leg o' mutton—just a bit cut off the end,
Oh, isn't it nice and jolly to be whalin' in the
    bend?

I have a little book and some papers for to
    read,
Plenty of matches and a good supply of weed;
I wouldn't be a squatter, as beside me fire I sit
With a paper in me hand and me old clay lit.

When shearin' time comes, I'm in all me glory
    then;
I saddle up me moke and I soon secure a pen;
I canter through the valley and gallop o'er the
    plain;
I shoot a turkey, stick a pig, and off to camp
    again.

FOUR LITTLE JOHNNY CAKES

Hur - rah for the Lach - lan, boys, and join me in a cheer; That's the

place to go to make an eas - y cheque ev - 'ry year; With a

toad - skin in me pock - et I bor - rowed from a friend, Oh,

is - n't it nice and co - sy to be camp - in' in the bend? With me

lit - tle round flour bag sit - tin' on a stump, Me

lit - tle tea and sug - ar bag a - look - ing nice and plump; With a

93

FOUR LITTLE JOHNNY CAKES

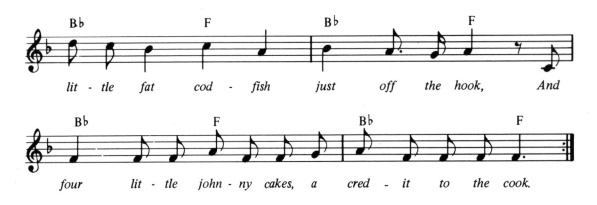

lit - tle fat cod - fish just off the hook, And

four lit - tle john - ny cakes, a cred - it to the cook.

TOAD-SKIN — a pound note, equivalent of two dollars

MURPHIES — potatoes

SNAVELLED — stole

WHALING — loafing. A 'whaler' is a particularly lazy tramp or swaggie.

MOKE — horse

NECESSITY THE MOTHER OF INVENTION.

SWAGSMAN: "If we stretched a line from the fence to that tree we could get any amount of watches off the coves as got drowned in the flood."

ROVER NO MORE

Usually known as 'The Wild Rover', 'Rover No More', as Paterson called it, is one of the most popular folksongs in the English language. Every English-speaking country has numerous rollicking versions of the song. This is one of ours, as collected by Paterson.

Oh, I've been a wild rover this many a year,
And I've spent all my money on whisky and
        beer;
But now I'm returning with gold in great
        store,
And I never shall play the wild rover no more.

Chorus
And it's no, no, never; never no more;
I never shall play the wild rover no more!

I dropt into a shanty I used to frequent
And I told the landlady my money was spent;
I asked her for credit; she answered me 'Nay!
Such a custom as yours I can get ev'ry day.'

Then I drew from my pocket ten sovereigns
        bright
And the landlady's eyes opened wide with
        delight;
Said she 'I have whisky and wines of the best,
And the words that I told you were only in
        jest.'

I'll go home to my parents; confess what I've
        done;
And I'll ask them to pardon their prodigal son;
And if they will do so, as often before,
Then I never shall play the wild rover no more.

ROVER NO MORE

Oh, I've been a wild rov-er this ma-ny a year, And I've
spent all my mon-ey on whis-ky and beer; But
now I'm re-turn-ing with gold in great store, And I
nev-er shall play the wild rov-er no more. And it's
no, no, nev-er; nev-er no more; I____
nev-er shall play the wild rov-er no more!

THE OLD KEG
OF RUM

Another celebration of that most Australian of pastimes—drinking! There is also a version of this song which involves shearers instead of the farm workers mentioned here in the second verse. The shearing version goes:

> There was Bluey Watt, the Breaker and old Tommy Hines,
> And Little Joe, the Ringer, who now in glory shines.

When harvesting or shearing was over it was the custom, as it is throughout most of the world, to have a lengthy party. In Australia this became known as a 'spree'.

My name is old Jack Palmer,
I'm a man of olden days,
And so I wish to sing a song
To you of olden praise;
To tell of merry friends of old
When we were gay and young;
How we sat and sang together
Round the Old Keg of Rum.

Chorus
Oh! the Old Keg of Rum! the Old Keg of
    Rum!
How we sat and sang together
Round the Old Keg of Rum.

There was I and Jack the ploughboy,
Jem Moore and old Tom Hines,
And poor old Tom the fiddler,
Who now in glory shines;

And several more of our old chums,
Who shine in Kingdom Come,
We all associated round the
Old Keg of Rum.

Chorus
Oh! the Old Keg of Rum! the Old Keg of
    Rum!
We all associated round the
Old Keg of Rum.

And when harvest time was over,
And we'd get our harvest fee,
We'd meet, and quickly rise the keg,
And then we'd have a spree.
We'd sit and sing together
Till we got that blind and dumb
That we couldn't find the bunghole
Of the Old Keg of Rum.

THE OLD KEG OF RUM

My name is old Jack Pal-mer, I'm a man of old-en days, ___ And so I wish to sing a song To you of old-en praise; ___ To tell of mer-ry friends of old when we were gay and young; How we sat and sang to-geth-er round the Old Keg of Rum. Oh! the Old Keg of Rum! the Old Keg of Rum! How we sat and sang to-geth-er round the Old Keg of Rum.

THE OLD KEG OF RUM

Chorus
Oh! the Old Keg of Rum! the Old Keg of
    Rum!
That we couldn't find the bunghole
Of the Old Keg of Rum.

It's jovially together, boys—
We'd laugh, we'd chat, we'd sing;
Sometimes we'd have a little row
Some argument would bring.
And oft-times in a scrimmage, boys,
I've corked it with my thumb,
To keep the life from leaking
From the Old Keg of Rum.

Chorus
Oh! the Old Keg of Rum! the Old Keg of
    Rum!
To keep the life from leaking
From the Old Keg of Rum.

But when our spree was ended, boys,
And waking from a snooze,
For to give another dram
The old keg would refuse.
We'd rap it with our knuckles—
If it sounded like a drum,
We'd know the life and spirit
Had left the Old Keg of Rum.

Chorus
Oh! the Old Keg of Rum! the Old Keg of
    Rum!

We'd know the life and spirit
Had left the Old Keg of Rum.

Those happy days have passed away,
I've seen their pleasures fade;
And many of our good old friends
Have with old times decayed.
But still, when on my travels, boys,
If I meet with an old chum,
We will sigh, in conversation,
Of the Grand Old Keg of Rum.

Chorus
Oh! the Old Keg of Rum! the Old Keg of
    Rum!
We will sigh, in conversation,
Of the Grand Old Keg of Rum.

So now, kind friends, I end my song,
I hope we'll meet again,
And, as I've tried to please you all,
I hope you won't complain.
You younger folks who learn my song,
Will perhaps in years to come,
Remember old Jack Palmer
And the Old Keg of Rum.

Chorus
Oh! the Old Keg of Rum! the Old Keg of
    Rum!
Remember old Jack Palmer
And the Old Keg of Rum.

A RUM DEFINITION.

PUBLICAN (*out West, to disgusted swagsman-customer*): "So you don't like that rum? What sort of rum *do* yer like, then?"

SWAGSMAN: "Well, I like good hot stuff what bites—that's like swallering a cat and pulling her back by the tail—bite all the way down and scratch all the way back."

A SKETCH IN DROUGHT-TIME.

TRAVELLER: "Got any washing-gear here for sale?"

STOREKEEPER: "Yes, sir, we have every toilet requisite."

TRAVELLER: "Then give us a bar of soap and a——horse-rasp, and I'll go down to the Guv'ment dam."

The Shearers
and the Shorn

Your backs well bent, blows long and clean,
that's what they want to see . . .

FLASH JACK
FROM GUNDAGAI

Paterson's own notes to this popular song probably explain it well enough:

> *I've pinked 'em with the Wolseleys and I've rushed with B-bows, too.* Wolseleys and B-bows are respectively machines and hand shears, and 'pinking' means that he had shorn the sheep so closely that the pink skin showed through.
>
> *I rung Cudjingie shed, and blued it in a week*, i.e., he was the ringer or fastest shearer of the shed, and he dissipated the earnings in a single week's drunkenness.
>
> *Whalin' up the Lachlan.* In the old days there was an army of 'sundowners' or professional loafers who walked from station to station, ostensibly to look for work, but without any idea of accepting it. These nomads often followed up and down certain rivers, and would camp for days and fish for cod in the bends of the river. Hence whaling up the Lachlan.

I've shore at Burrabogie, and I've shore at
    Toganmain,
I've shore at big Willandra and upon the old
    Coleraine,
But before the shearin' was over I've wished
    myself back again
Shearin' for old Tom Patterson, on the One-
    Tree Plain.

Chorus
All among the wool, boys, (all among the
    wool),
Keep your wide blades full, boys, (keep your
    wide blades full).
I can do a respectable tally myself whenever I
    like to try,
But they know me round the backblocks as
    Flash Jack from Gundagai.

I've shore at big Willandra and I've shore at
    Tilberoo,
And once I drew my blades, my boys, upon the
    famed Barcoo,
At Cowan Downs and Trida, as far as
    Moulamein,
But I always was glad to get back again to
    the One-Tree Plain.

I've pinked 'em with the Wolseleys and I've
    rushed with B-bows, too,
And shaved 'em in the grease, my boys, with
    the grass seed showing through,
But I never slummed my pen, my lads,
    whate'er it might contain,
While shearin' for old Tom Patterson, on the
    One-Tree Plain.

FLASH JACK FROM GUNDAGAI

I've shore at Bur - ra - bo - gie, and I've shore at To - gan - main, I've shore at big Wil - lan - dra and up - on the old Cole - raine,_____ But be - fore the shear - in' was o - ver I've wished my - self back a - gain_____ Shear - in' for old Tom Pat - ter - son, on the One - Tree Plain.

FLASH JACK FROM GUNDAGAI

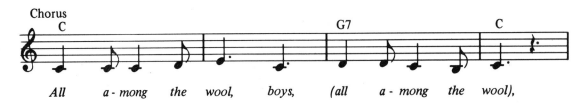

All   a - mong   the   wool,   boys,   (all   a - mong   the   wool),

Keep   your   wide   blades   full,   boys,   (keep   your   wide   blades

full). _____   I   can   do   a   res - pec - ta - ble   tal - ly   my - self   when -

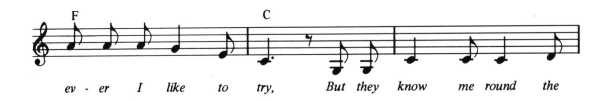

ev - er   I   like   to   try,   But   they   know   me   round   the

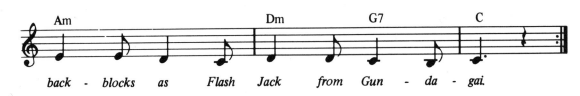

back - blocks   as   Flash   Jack   from   Gun - da - gai.

FLASH JACK FROM GUNDAGAI

I've been whalin' up the Lachlan, and I've
      dossed in Cooper's Creek,
And once I rung Cudjingie shed, and blued
      it in a week.
But when Gabriel blows his trumpet, lads, I'll
      catch the morning train,
And I'll push for old Tom Patterson's on the
      One-Tree Plain.

WHY HE WENT OUTSIDE.

1. SHEARER (who has got angry about the obstinacy of a ram): "Mister, will you hold him for a minute?"

2. MINISTER: "Certainly, my good man."

3. MINISTER: "Why did you go outside?"

SHEARER: "Why, don't you see, if I swear in the shed I'm fined 10s., so I went outside."

THE PLAINS OF RIVERINE

1897 was the year of Queen Victoria's Diamond Jubilee, a cause of great celebrations throughout the Empire. The song presumably dates from that year, during which the squatters of the Riverina region of New South Wales apparently agreed to 'pay the pound'. Paterson explains:

> *A pound a hundred* is the price for shearing sheep, and several bitterly fought-out strikes have taken place about it.
> *We'll take no topknots off this year nor trim them to the toes.* Owing to the amiability of the squatters and the excellence of the season, the shearers intend to leave some of the wool on the sheep, i.e., the topknots on the head and the wool down on the legs.

I've never heard 'The Plains of Riverine' sung, so I set it to the tune of a fine song called 'The Banks of the Condamine'. A few small changes to some of the lines have made this version more suitable for singing.

I have come to tell the glorious news you'll all
    be glad to hear
Of the pleasant alterations that are taking place
    this year.
So kindly pay attention, and I'll pass the
    whisper round,
The squatters of their own free will this year
    will pay the pound.

This is a year of great prosperity, that
    everybody knows,
We'll take no topknots off this year, nor trim
    them to the toes,
But a level cut for a level pound, and the
    rations thrown in free.
That's how the squatters say they'll keep their
    Sovereign's Jubilee.

And kind Providence once more has sent the
    sweet, refreshing rains.
The trefoil and the barley-grass wave high
    upon the plains,
The tanks are overflowing and the saltbush
    fresh and green,
It's a pleasure for to ramble o'er the plains of
    Riverine.

Once more upon the rippling lake the wild
    swan flaps her wing.
Out in the lignum swamps once more frogs
    croak and crickets sing.
Once more the wild fowl, sporting midst the
    crab-holes, may be seen,
For prosperity is hovering o'er the plains of
    Riverine.

THE PLAINS OF RIVERINE

THE PLAINS OF RIVERINE

'Twill be a year of full and plenty for those
    backblock pioneers,
Though behind each scrub and saltbush you can
    spot the bunny's ears;
And although the price for scalps is not so high
    as it has been,
Yet the bunny snappers they will thrive on
    the plains of Riverine.

You should see the jolly teamsters how with
    joy their faces beam,
As they talk about the crowfoot, carrots,
    crab-holes, and their team.
They tell you that this year they do intend to
    steer sixteen,
They'll show the cockies how to plough the
    plains of Riverine.

Yes, in more respects than one it is a year of
    joy and glee,
And the news of our prosperity has crossed the
    briny sea.
Once more the Maorilander and the Tassy will
    be seen
Cooking johnny cakes and jimmies on the
    plains of Riverine.

They will gather like a regiment to the beating
    of the drum,
But it matters not to us from whence our
    future pen-mates come.
From New Zealand's snow-clad summits or
    Tasmania's meadows green,
We'll always make them welcome on the plains
    of Riverine.

From her rocky peaks Monaro will send her
    champions bold;
Victoria will send her cockies, too, her honour
    to uphold.
They'll be here from Cunnamulla, and the
    rolling downs between,
For this is the real convincing ground, these
    plains of Riverine.

I have a message to deliver now, before I say
    farewell,
Some news which all the squatters have
    commissioned me to tell;
Your backs well bent, blows long and clean,
    that's what they want to see,
That your tallies may do you credit in this year
    of Jubilee.

TO STEER SIXTEEN — to steer sixteen horses (or bullocks) on a team, a difficult feat

"AND USE THEM IF NECESSARY."

"Brisbane, Thursday. Evidence is accumulating that the strike is fast approaching a close. The Colonial Secretary has received a letter from the country cadet corps expressing disgust at the recent cowardly acts of the unionist shearers and offering to shoulder their rifles, and use them if necessary."—*Daily paper*

THE OLD BULLOCK DRAY

A bullock driver's idea of proposing marriage! Paterson's notes to this song probably explain it best:

A *paddymelon* is a small and speedy marsupial, a sort of poor relation of the great kangaroo family.

Calling at the depot to get an offsider. Female immigrants were housed at the depot on arrival, and many found husbands within a few hours of their landing. The minstrel, therefore, proposes to call at the depot to get himself a wife from among the immigrants. An offsider is a bullock-driver's assistant — one who walks on the offside of the team and flogs the bullocks on that side when occasion arises. The word afterwards came to mean an assistant of any kind.

Jack Robertson. Sir John Robertson, as he afterwards became, was a well-known politician who believed in Australians doing their best to populate their own country.

Budgery you — good fellow you.

Oh! the shearing is all over,
And the wool is coming down,
And I mean to get a wife, boys,
When I go up to town.
Everything that has two legs
Represents itself in view,
From the little paddymelon
To the bucking kangaroo.

Chorus
So it's roll up your blankets,
And let's make a push,
I'll take you up the country,
And I'll show you the bush.
I'll be bound you won't get
Such a chance another day,
So come and take possession
Of my old bullock dray.

Now, I've saved up a good cheque,
I mean to buy a team,
And when I get a wife, boys,
I'll be all-serene;
For, calling at the depot,
They say there's no delay
To get an offsider
For the old bullock dray.

Oh! we'll live like fighting cocks,
For good living, I'm your man.
We'll have leather-jacks, johnny cakes,
And fritters in the pan;
Or if you'd like some fish
I'll catch you some soon,
For we'll bob for barramundies
Round the banks of a lagoon.

THE OLD BULLOCK DRAY

Oh! the shear - ing is all o - ver, And the wool is com - ing

down, And I mean to get a wife, boys, when I go up to

town. Ev' - ry - thing that has two legs Re - pre - sents it - self in

view, From the lit - tle pad - dy - me - lon to the

buck - ing kan - ga - roo. So it's roll up your

blan - kets, And let's make a push, I'll take you up the

THE OLD BULLOCK DRAY

coun - try, And I'll show you the bush. I'll be
bound you won't get Such a chance an-oth-er day, So
come and take pos - ses - sion Of my old bul - lock dray.

Oh! yes, of beef and damper
I take care we have enough,
And we'll boil in the bucket
Such a whopper of a duff,
And our friends will dance
To the honour of the day,
To the music of the bells
Around the old bullock dray.

Oh! we'll have plenty girls,
We must mind that.
There'll be flash little Maggie,
And backjumping Pat.
There'll be Stringybark Joe,
And Greenhide Mike.
Yes, my colonials, just
As many as you like.

Now we'll stop all immigration,
We won't need it any more;
We'll be having young natives,
Twins by the score.
And I wonder what the devil
Jack Robertson would say
If he saw us promenading
Round the old bullock dray.

Oh! it's time I had an answer,
If there's one to be had,
I wouldn't treat that steer
In the body half as bad;
But he takes as much notice
Of me, upon my soul,
As that old blue stag
Offside in the pole.

THE OLD BULLOCK DRAY

Oh! to tell a lot of lies,
You know, it is a sin,
But I'll go up country
And marry a black gin.
Oh! 'Baal gammon white feller',
This is what she'll say,
'Budgery you
And your old-bullock dray.'

LEATHER-JACK — a flat cake of flour and water, fried in a pan
BAAL GAMMON — Aboriginal pidgin = 'You're not joking'

THE MURRUMBIDGEE
SHEARER

'The Murrumbidgee Shearer' is a fine, swaggering song with a tune to match. It tells a far from uncommon story of bush life in eastern Australia during the second half of the last century. Whoever the 'Murrumbidgee Shearer' was he had a chequered career that included gold prospecting, burning the sheds of uncooperative squatters, 'touching' the shepherd's scarce rations and robbing gold escorts. He doesn't seem to have had much time for shearing. Not surprisingly, he ends up doing ten years in the notorious Cockatoo Island prison. The song ends with the shearer looking back over his career with relish and perhaps a touch of sadness at the passing of 'the good old time'.

Come, all you jolly natives, and I'll relate to
    you
Some of my observations—adventures, too,
    a few.
I've travelled about the country for miles full
    many a score,
And oft-times would have hungered, but for
    the cheek I bore.

I've coasted on the Barwon, low down the
    Darling, too,
I've been on the Murrumbidgee, and out on
    the Paroo;
I've been on all the diggings, boys, from
    famous Ballarat;
I've loafed upon the Lachlan and fossicked
    Lambing Flat.

I went up to a squatter, and asked him for a
    feed,
But the knowledge of my hunger was
    swallowed by his greed.
He said I was a loafer and for work had no
    desire,
And so, to do him justice, I set his shed on
    fire.

Oh, yes, I've touched the shepherd's hut, of
    sugar, tea, and flour;
And a tender bit of mutton I always could
    devour.
I went up to a station, and there I got a
    job;
Plunged in the store, and hooked it, with a
    very tidy lob.

THE MURRUMBIDGEE SHEARER

Come, all you jolly na___tives, and I'll re-late to you___ Some of my ob-ser-va-tions ad-ven-tures, too, a few.___ I've tra-velled a-bout the coun___-try for miles full ma-ny a score,___ And oft-times would have hun___-gered, but for the cheek I bore.

THE MURRUMBIDGEE SHEARER

Oh, yes, my jolly dandies, I've done it on the
    cross.
Although I carry bluey now, I've sweated many
    a horse.
I've helped to ease the escort of many's the
    ounce of gold;
The traps have often chased me, more times
    than can be told.

Oh, yes, the traps have chased me, been
    frightened out of their stripes;
They never could have caught me, they feared
    my cure for gripes.
And well they knew I carried it, which they
    had often seen

A-glistening in my flipper, chaps, a patent pill
    machine.

I've been hunted like a panther into my
    mountain lair.
Anxiety and misery my grim companions there.
I've planted in the scrub, my boys, and fed on
    kangaroo,
And wound up my avocations by ten years on
    Cockatoo.

So you can understand, my boys, just from this
    little rhyme,
I'm a Murrumbidgee shearer, and one of the
    good old time.

FOSSICKED — prospected for gold
BLUEY — swag
TRAPS — mounted troopers or police
PATENT PILL MACHINE — pistol
COCKATOO — Cockatoo Island prison, Sydney

VERBAL CASH.

BLUEY: "How about a contract?"

MR. FLEECE: "Oh, never mind that, we'll have a verbal contract."

BLUEY: "Scuse me, boss. Last time I had a verbal contract, I drew verbal wages."

ANOTHER FALL OF RAIN

Paterson had a few words to say about 'Another Fall of Rain':

> The strain of shearing is very severe on the wrists, and the ringer or fastest shearer is very apt to go in the wrists, especially at the beginning of a season. Hence the desire of the shearers for a fall of rain after a long stretch of hot weather.

This song may be a variant of John Shaw Neilson's poem, 'Waiting for the Rain', or Neilson's poem may have been a reworking of an existing bush song. We'll probably never know, just as we'll probably never know if Gibson's 'A Ballad Of Queensland' came before the song 'Sam Holt' (see notes to this song) or even if Paterson's own poem 'A Bushman's Song', was based on some fragments of an old bush song he had picked up somewhere or other.

The weather had been sultry for a fortnight's
    time or more,
And the shearers had been driving might and
    main,
For some had got the century who'd ne'er got
    it before,
And now all hands were waiting for the rain.

Chorus
For the boss is getting rusty and the ringer's
    caving in,
For his bandaged wrist is aching with the pain,
And the second man, I fear, will make it hot
    for him,
Unless we have another fall of rain.

A few had taken quarters and were coiling in
    their bunks
When we shore the six-tooth wethers from the
    plain.

And if the sheep get harder, then a few more
    men will funk,
Unless we get another fall of rain.

But the sky is clouding over, and the thunder's
    muttering loud,
And the clouds are driving eastward o'er the
    plain,
And I see the lightning flashing from the edge
    of yon black cloud,
And I hear the gentle patter of the rain.

So, lads, put on your stoppers, and let us to
    the hut,
Where we'll gather round and have a friendly
    game,
While some are playing music and some play
    ante-up,
And some are gazing outwards at the rain.

ANOTHER FALL OF RAIN

The wea - ther had been sul - try for a fort - night's time or more, And the shear - ers had been driv - ing might and main, For some had got the cen - tu - ry who'd ne'er got it be - fore, And__ now all hands were wait - ing for the rain. For the boss is get - ting rus - ty and the ring - er's cav - ing in, For his

ANOTHER FALL OF RAIN

band - aged wrist is ach - ing with the pain, And the
sec - ond man, I fear,___ will make it hot for
him, Un - less we have an - oth - er fall of rain.

But now the rain is over, let the pressers spin
    the screw,
Let the teamsters back the wagons in again,
And we'll block the classer's table by the way
    we'll put them through,
For everything is merry since the rain.

And the boss he won't be rusty when his
    sheep they all are shorn
And the ringer's wrist won't ache much with
    the pain
Of pocketing his cheque for fifty pounds or more,
And the second man will press him hard again.

CENTURY — 100 sheep shorn in a day
STOPPERS — safety guard for shears when not being used
ANTE-UP — card game

THE SQUATTER OF TO-DAY.

WOOL PRESSER: "Pretty hard work, sir."

SQUATTER: "Yes—well, not so *very* hard."

W. P.: "I'd like to change billets with you, sir."

SQUATTER: "Well, if you give me £50 and a pair of horses, and accept my liabilities and the station, I'll swop."

GOORIANAWA

'Goorianawa' is probably one of the finest Australian work songs ever collected. It has a long and complicated history, but basically it's about the hardest shed that anyone ever shore, the legendary Goorianawa station near Barradine, New South Wales. The other people and places mentioned in the song are stations and station owners or managers notorious among shearers for their hard conditions and terms of employment.

This is one of the songs Paterson had heard in the bush but was never able to find. Luckily, it has since turned up.

I've been many years a shearer, and fancied I
    could shear,
I've shore for Rouse of Guntawang and always
    missed the spear;
I've shore for Nicholas Bayly, and I declare to
    you,
That on his pure Merinos I could always
    struggle through.

Chorus
But, oh my! I never saw before
The way we had to knuckle down at
    Goorianawa.

I've been shearing down the Bogan, as far as
    Dandaloo,
For good old Reid of Tabratong I've often cut
    a few;
Haddon Rig and Quambone, and even
    Wingadee—
I could close my shears at six o'clock with a
    quiet century.

I've been shearing on the Goulburn side and
    down at Douglas Park,
Where every day 'twas 'Wool away!' and
    'Toby' did his work.
I've shore for General Stewart, whose tomb is
    on The Mount,
And the sprees I've had with Scrammy Jack are
    more than I can count.

I've shore for John McMaster down on
    Rockedgial Creek,
And I could always dish him up with thirty
    score a week.
I've shore at Terramungamine and on the
    Talbragar,
And I ran McDermott for the cobbler when we
    shore at Buckingbar.

I've been shearing at Eugowra—I'll never
    forget the name,
Where Gardiner robbed the escort that from
    the Lachlan came.

GOORIANAWA

I've been ma-ny years a shear-er, and fan-cied I could shear, I've shore for Rouse of Gun-ta-wang and al-ways missed the spear; I've shore for Nich'-las Bay-ly and I de-clare to you, That on his pure Me-ri-nos I could al-ways strug-gle through. But, oh my! I ne-ver saw be-fore, The way we had to knu-ckle down at Goo-ri-a-na-wa.

GOORIANAWA

I've shore for Bob Fitzgerald down at the
    Dabee Rocks,
McPhillamy of Charlton and Mister Henry
    Cox.

I rang the shed at Nardoo, I rang at Gumin
    too,
And Jacky Howe at Mulga Downs just beat
    me by a few.
The sheep were big and wrinkly, the wool was
    tough as hell,
I made him keep his head down but he caught
    me on the bell.

I shore along the Narran, the Warrego and
    Paroo,
And Jacky was the only man that could ever
    put me through.

I've shorn in every woolshed from the Barwon
    to the sea.
I got speared at Goorianawa before I'd barbered
    three.

That was in the good old days—you might
    have heard them say
How Skellycorn from Bathurst rode to Sydney
    in a day.
But now I'm broken-mouthed and my
    shearing's at an end,
And though they called me 'Whalebone' I was
    never known to bend.

Last chorus
But, spare me flamin' days! I never saw before
The way we had to knuckle down at
    Goorianawa.

THE SPEAR — the sack. The meaning here is that the shearer in the song always performed well enough to
    avoid losing his job.
TOBY — a 'raddle' or 'ruddle' stick used by the owner to mark sheep shorn unsatisfactorily. The shearer
    was not paid for such sheep and the system was the cause of much friction between the shearers
    and the employers.
THE COBBLER — last sheep of the day to be shorn
RANG THE SHED — the ringer is the fastest shearer in the shed

DUFF AND MACDUFF.

SMART SHEARER: "Dinner ready, MacDuff?"

CHOLERIC COOK: "No, deener's no ready, and my name's no MacDuff."

SHEARER: "Mak *no* duff then—is *that* it?"

Stockmen
and Drovers

Be ye stockmen or no, to my story give ear ...

MUSTERING SONG

A song about the hazards of mustering half-wild cattle scattered across hundreds of square kilometres, all of them dangerous. This song, with its jolly tune ('Early in the Morning'), makes a joke of the rigours continually experienced by stockmen during a muster.

The boss last night in the hut did say—
'We start to muster at break of day;
So be up first thing, and don't be slow;
Saddle your horses and off you go.'

Chorus
So early in the morning,
So early in the morning,
So early in the morning,
Before the break of day.

Such a night in the yard there never was seen
(The horses were fat and the grass was
     green);
Bursting of girths and slipping of packs
As the stockmen saddled the fastest hacks.

Across the plain we jog along
Over gully, swamp, and billabong;
We drop on a mob pretty lively, too;
We round 'em up and give 'em a slue.

Now the scrub grows thick and the cattle are
     wild,
A regular caution to this 'ere child—
A new-chum man on an old-chum horse,

Who sails through the scrub as a matter of
    course.

I was close up stuck in a rotten bog;
I got a buster jumping a log;
I found this scouting rather hot,
So I joined the niggers with the lot we'd got.

A long-haired shepherd we chanced to meet
With a water-bag, billy, and dog complete;
He came too close to a knocked-up steer
Who up a sapling made him clear.

Now on every side we faintly hear
The crack of the stockwhip drawing near;
To the camp the cattle soon converge,
As from the thick scrub they emerge.

We hastily comfort the inner man
With the warm contents of the billy-can;
The beef and damper are passed about
Before we tackle the cutting out.

We're at it now—that bally calf
Would surely make a sick man laugh;
The silly fool can't take a joke;
I hope some day in the drought he'll croak.

MUSTERING SONG

The boss last night in the hut did say 'We start to mus - ter at break of day; So be up first thing, and don't be slow; Sad - dle your hors - es and off you go.' So ear - ly in the morn - ing, So ear - ly in the morn - ing, So ear - ly in the morn - ing, Be - fore the break of day.

MUSTERING SONG

We've got 'em now—the cows and calves
(Things here are never done by halves);
Strangers, workers, and milkers, too,
Of scrubbers also not a few.

It's getting late, we'd better push;
'Tis a good long way across the bush,
And the mob to drive are middling hard;
I do not think we'll reach the yard.

SLUE — to head or turn a mob of cattle using a specially trained dog
BUSTER — a fall, accident
STRANGERS — strays
WORKERS — strong steers
MILKERS — milk cows
SCRUBBERS — steers which live apart from the rest of the mob

"THERE'S LIFE FOR Y'!"

THE OVERLANDER

Especially popular in Queensland, this song is also known as 'The Queensland Drover' in some of its many versions. Like the other songs about cattle droving in this book, and elsewhere, it is a robust and rousing blend of words and music that perfectly expresses the happy-go-lucky spirit of the drovers.

There's a trade you all know well—
   It's bringing cattle over—
I'll tell you all about the time
   When I became a drover.
I made up my mind to try the spec,
   To the Clarence I did wander,
And bought a mob of duffers there
   To begin as an overlander.

Chorus
Pass the wine cup round, my boys;
   Don't let the bottle stand there,
For tonight we'll drink the health
   Of every overlander.

Next morning counted the cattle,
   Saw the outfit ready to start,
Saw all the lads well mounted,
   And their swags put in a cart.
All kinds of men I had
   From Germany, France, and Flanders;
Lawyers, doctors, good and bad,
   In the mob of overlanders.

Next morning I set out
   When the grass was green and young;

And they swore they'd break my snout
   If I did not move along.
I said, 'You're very hard;
   Take care, don't raise my dander,
For I'm a regular knowing card,
   The Queensland overlander.'

'Tis true we pay no licence,
   And our run is rather large;
'Tis not often they can catch us,
   So they cannot make a charge.
They think we live on store beef,
   But no, I'm not a gander;
When a good fat stranger joins the mob,
   'He'll do,' says the overlander.

One day a squatter rode up.
   Says he, 'You're on my run;
I've got two boys as witnesses.
   Consider your stock in pound.'
I tried to coax, then bounce him,
   But my tin I had to squander,
For he put threepence a head
   On the mob of the overlander.

THE OVERLANDER

There's a trade you all know well It's_ bring - ing cat - tle

o - ver I'll _ tell you all a - bout the time When

I be - came a dro - ver. I made up my mind to

try the spec, To the Cla - rence I did wan - der, And

bought a mob of duf - fers there To be - gin as an o - ver -

THE OVERLANDER

lan - der   Pass   the   wine __ cup __ round, my   boys;

Don't   let   the   bot - tle   stand there,   For   to - night   we'll   drink   the

health   Of   ev - 'ry   o - ver - lan - der.

The pretty girls in Brisbane
  Were hanging out their duds.
I wished to have a chat with them,
  So steered straight for the tubs.
Some dirty urchins saw me,
  And soon they raised my dander,
Crying, 'Mother, quick! take in the clothes,
  Here comes an overlander!'

In town we drain the wine cup,
  And go to see the play,
And never think to be hard up
  For how to pass the day.
Each has a sweetheart there,
  Dressed out in all her grandeur—
Dark eyes and jet black flowing hair.
  'She's a plum,' says the overlander.

SPEC — gamble
DUFFERS — cattle in this instance, but more usually rustlers
DANDER — temper
TIN — money

THE DYING STOCKMAN

Dying sailors, cowboys, timber-cutters and airmen litter the field of English-language folksong; 'The Dying Stockman' is one of a number of Australian variants of this widespread and popular theme. This particular rendition of the song that Paterson published bears signs of having been 'touched up' a little, rather in the style of 'The Stockman's Last Bed'.

A strapping young stockman lay dying,
His saddle supporting his head;
His two mates around him were crying,
As he rose on his pillow and said:

Chorus
'Wrap me up with my stockwhip and blanket,
And bury me deep down below,
Where the dingoes and crows can't molest me,
In the shade where the coolibahs grow.

'Oh! had I the flight of the bronzewing,
Far o'er the plains would I fly,
Straight to the land of my childhood,
And there I would lay down and die.

'Then cut down a couple of saplings,
Place one at my head and my toe,
Carve on them cross, stockwhip, and saddle,
To show there's a stockman below.

'Hark! there's the wail of a dingo,
Watchful and weird—I must go,
For it tolls the death-knell of the stockman
From the gloom of the scrub down below.

'There's tea in the battered old billy;
Place the pannikins out in a row,
And we'll drink to the next merry meeting,
In the place where all good fellows go.

'And oft in the shades of the twilight,
When the soft winds are whispering low,
And the darkening shadows are falling,
Sometimes think of the stockman below.'

THE DYING STOCKMAN

A ___ strap - ping young stock - man lay dy - ing, ___

___ His sad - dle sup - port - ing his head; ___

___ His two mates a - round him were cry - ing, ___

___ As he rose on his pil - low and said: ___

Chorus

___ 'Wrap me up with my stock - whip and blank - et, ___

___ And bu - ry me deep down be - low, ___

THE DYING STOCKMAN

Where the din - goes and crows can't mo - lest me,___

In the shade where the coo - li - bahs grow.

FRANK P MAHONY 1892

A THOUSAND MILES AWAY

This lively song celebrates the quality and quantity of Australian cattle, frozen and exported around the world. The same tune has been used for a number of other Australian songs, including 'The Old Palmer Song' and 'Ten Thousand Miles Away'. Readers may be more familiar with the tune as the basis of George Dreyfus's theme music for the ABC-TV series, *Rush*, which flickered across our screens a few years ago.

Hurrah for the Roma railway! Hurrah for
    Cobb and Co.,
And oh! for a good fat horse or two to carry
    me Westward Ho—
To carry me Westward Ho! my boys, that's
    where the cattle stray,
On the far Barcoo, where they eat nardoo, a
    thousand miles away.

Chorus
Then give your horses rein across the open
    plain,
We'll ship our meat both sound and sweet, nor
    care what some folks say;
And frozen we'll send home the cattle that now
    roam
On the far Barcoo and the Flinders too, a
    thousand miles away.

Knee-deep in grass we've got to pass—for the
    truth I'm bound to tell—
Where in three weeks the cattle get as fat as
    they can swell;
As fat as they can swell, my boys, a thousand
    pounds they weigh,
On the far Barcoo, where they eat nardoo, a
    thousand miles away.

No Yankee hide e'er grew outside such beef as
    we can freeze;
No Yankee pastures make such steers as we
    send o'er the seas—
As we send o'er the seas, my boys, a thousand
    pounds they weigh—
From the far Barcoo, where they eat nardoo, a
    thousand miles away.

NARDOO — berry from which the Aborigines made flour and an intoxicating drink

A THOUSAND MILES AWAY

Hur - rah for the Ro - ma rail - way! Hur - rah for Cobb and

Co., And oh! for a good fat horse or two to

car - ry me West - ward Ho To car - ry me West - ward

Ho! my boys, that's where the cat - tle stray, On the

far Bar - coo, where they eat nar - doo, a thous - and miles a - way.

THE MARANOA DROVERS

Paterson gives 'Little Sally Walters' as the air for this song (more commonly called 'The Sandy Maranoa') but I prefer the more spirited 'Little Old Log Cabin in the Lane' tune to which it is usually sung. The words of this evocative song about cattle droving in Queensland and New South Wales have been attributed to Mr A. W. Davis, a Queensland drover during the late nineteenth century. Whether he composed it or not the song is a fine portrait of the rough and tumble open air life of the drover, if perhaps a touch on the romantic rather than the realistic side.

The night is dark and stormy, and the sky is
    clouded o'er;
Our horses we will mount and ride away,
To watch the squatters' cattle through the
    darkness of the night,
And we'll keep them on the camp till break of
    day.

Chorus
For we're going, going, going to Gunnedah so
    far,
And we'll soon be into sunny New South
    Wales;
We shall bid farewell to Queensland, with its
    swampy coolibah—
Happy drovers from the sandy Maranoa.

When the fires are burning bright through the
    darkness of the night,
And the cattle camping quiet, well, I'm sure
That I wish for two o'clock when I call the
    other watch—
This is droving from the sandy Maranoa.

Our beds made on the ground, we are sleeping
    all so sound
When we're wakened by the distant thunder's
    roar,
And the lightning's vivid flash, followed by an
    awful crash—
It's rough on drovers from the sandy Maranoa.

We are up at break of day, and we're all soon
    on the way,
For we always have to go ten miles or more;
It don't do to loaf about, or the squatter will
    come out—
He's strict on drovers from the sandy Maranoa.

We shall soon be on the Moonie, and we'll
    cross the Barwon, too;
Then we'll be out upon the rolling plains once
    more;
We'll shout 'Hurrah! for old Queensland, with
    its swampy coolibah,
And the cattle that come off the Maranoa.'

THE MARANOA DROVERS

The night is dark and storm-y, and the sky is cloud-ed o'er; Our
hors - es we will mount and ride a - way, To
watch the squat - ter's cat - tle through the dark - ness of the night, And we'll
keep them on the camp till break of day. For we're
go - ing, go - ing, go - ing to Gun - ned - ah so far, And we'll

THE MARANOA DROVERS

soon be in - to sun - ny New South Wales; We shall

bid fare - well to Queens - land, with its swamp - y coo - li - bah, Hap - py

drov — ers from the san — dy Ma — ra — noa.

THE STOCKMAN'S
LAST BED

Stockmen lived hazardous lives, it seems. Here's another dying stockman, though this unfortunate was more likely to have come from the manager's residence than from the hired hands' quarters. Accidents in the bush were no respecters of social class, and death is just as hard whether expressed in the flowery jackeroo language of this popular song or in the more down-to-earth lines of 'The Dying Stockman'.

Be ye stockmen or no, to my story give ear.
Alas! for poor Jack, no more shall we hear
The crack of his stockwhip, his steed's lively
    trot,
His clear 'Go ahead, boys', his jingling quart
    pot.

Chorus
For we laid him where wattles their sweet
    fragrance shed,
And the tall gum trees shadow the stockman's
    last bed.

Whilst drafting one day he was horned by a
    cow.
'Alas!' cried poor Jack, 'It's all up with me now,

For I never again shall my saddle regain,
Nor bound like a wallaby over the plain.'

His whip it is silent, his dogs they do mourn,
His steed looks in vain for his master's return;
No friend to bemoan him, unheeded he dies;
Save Australia's dark sons, few know where he
    lies.

Now, stockman, if ever on some future day
After the wild mob you happen to stray,
Tread softly where wattles their sweet fragrance
    spread,
Where alone and neglected poor Jack's bones
    are laid.

THE STOCKMAN'S LAST BED

Be ye stock - men or no, to my sto - ry give ear. A - las! for poor Jack, ___ no more shall we hear The crack of his stock - whip, his__ steed's live - ly trot, His clear 'Go a - head, boys', his jing - ling quart pot. For we laid him where wat - tles their sweet fra - grance shed, And the tall gum trees sha - dow the stock - man's last bed.

LISTENING

Bush Traditions, Larrikin Records LRF 007. Field recordings of Australian bush songs.

Freedom on the Wallaby, Larrikin Records LRF 112. Features Dave Dehugard, a fine interpreter of Australian folksong.

Game as Ned Kelly, Larrikin Records LRF 050. A selection of songs and other material about the Kellys, performed by some of Australia's finest folk artists.

Glenrowan to the Gulf, EMI SOEX 631. The Wild Colonial Boys; one of the earliest and best recordings by an Australian bush band.

The Great Australian Legend, Topic Records (UK) 12TS 203. Some familiar and not-so-familiar songs by the English folklorist, A. L. Lloyd.

The Original Bushwackers and Bullockies Band, Larrikin Records LRF 019. First album of the Bushwackers.

The Springtime it Brings on the Shearing, Larrikin Records LRF 022. A collection of shearing songs by Gary Shearston.

READING

Edwards, R., *The Big Book of Australian Folk Song*, Adelaide, 1976.

Manifold, J., *The Penguin Australian Song Book*, Ringwood, Vic., 1964.

Manifold, J., *Who Wrote the Ballads?*, Sydney, 1964.

Meredith, J., and H. Anderson, *Folksongs of Australia*, Sydney, 1967.

Scott, W., *The Second Penguin Australian Songbook*, Ringwood, Vic., 1980.

Stewart, D., and N. Keesing, *Australian Bush Ballads*, Melbourne, 1955 (words only).

Stewart, D., and N. Keesing, *Old Bush Songs*, Melbourne, 1957 (words only).

Ward, R., *The Australian Legend*, London, 1958.

Ward, R., *The Penguin Book of Australian Ballads*, Ringwood, Vic., 1964 (words only).